ERKS ON PARADE

First published in 2008 by

WOODFIELD PUBLISHING LTD
Bognor Regis ~ West Sussex ~ England ~ PO21 5EL
www.woodfieldpublishing.com

The right of Graham Wise
to be identified as Author of this work
has been asserted in accordance with
the Copyright, Designs and Patents Act 1988

ISBN 1-84683-063-X

ERKS ON PARADE

*A humorous look at the life of an
RAF Airman in the 1950s*

GRAHAM WISE

WITH ILLUSTRATIONS BY
ROY YATES

Woodfield

Woodfield Publishing Ltd

Woodfield House ~ Babsham Lane ~ Bognor Regis ~ West Sussex ~ PO21 5EL
telephone 01243 821234 ~ e-mail enquiries@woodfieldpublishing.co.uk

Interesting and informative books on a variety of subjects

For full details of all our published titles, visit our website at
www.woodfieldpublishing.co.uk

~ CONTENTS ~

*I am indebted to Roy Yates
for his excellent cartoons.*

*Roy, like me was proud to be
an "Erk" in the 1950s*

This should be suitable for your research.

1. Joining Up

"But *boys* cannot join the Wrens," said the strange-looking old man. It was Bob's turn for an interview with the Careers Officer visiting the school and Bob had said that he liked the odd-shaped hats worn by the Wrens and could he be a Wren?

Bob Wilson was now fourteen and his life was all about getting up to pranks with his mates, annoying old people and generally ignoring girls. He hadn't really thought about a career – that was for the 'swots' at school who always had their heads in books, were first to put up their hands when old Smithy asked a question and stayed behind to help teacher at the end of class. Bob was usually out of the classroom door before the bell stopped ringing.

It was 1951, the war was a distant memory and, better still, sweets were no longer rationed. Most of the schoolboys' fathers had returned from the war, including Bob's, although there were one or two boys at school, quite often the less well-dressed ones, that no longer had a dad. There was also Spotty Davis, who had never had a dad, but always seemed to have an uncle living at home, often an American one, so Spotty always had chewing gum, even when sweets were rationed.

Many of the boys did not know what they wanted to do when they left school, although most of them expected they would do the same job as their father. Frank Taylor's dad was a postman; everyone said he knew everybody's business by the envelopes they received. Sid Bishop's dad was a bus driver and Freddy Jones's dad worked in a garage. The Jones family always had a car parked in front of their house, although they never went anywhere in it and Freddy's dad always had the bonnet up. Norman Evans' dad had the most unpopular job and nobody would speak to him on his way home from work. He drove a tanker lorry with a square open box on the back and he drove from door to door, not delivering like the milkman or baker, but collecting. Not every house had flush toilets, a lot had an outside "privy" with a wooden seat and a bucket underneath that had to be emptied once a week. That was Stinker Evans' job; he would walk to the privy with an empty bucket, tip the full bucket into this and then empty his bucket into the square open container on the back of his lorry. Plenty of opportunity for the smell and sometimes the contents to spill out. Everyone knew Stinker and the bus conductors would make him stand on the platform under the stairs of the bus on his journey home. Bob had never visited Norman Evans' house.

Bob's Dad had worked for Bill Long, the local butcher, before the war and had gone back there when he was demobbed from the RAF. Old Ted the Manager had retired and Fred Wilson, Bob's father, had taken over as Manager. Bob sometimes helped out at the back of the shop after school or on Saturdays, although he was not allowed to get anywhere near anything sharp, probably because of his reputation for being a bit "accident prone". If something had never been broken before, then rest assured Bob would break it. The Taylors' dog had never bitten anyone in its 14 years on this earth – but it bit Bob – although it has to be added that Bob and Frank Martin were carrying out a rather unsavoury experiment on the poor animal at the time.

So here was Bob, 14 years old, not a care in the world and suddenly being asked to take his first steps towards becoming a grown-up. What was he going to do when he left school? Everyone assumed he would become a butcher like his dad and Bob did nothing to make them change their view. After all, why should he? He was young, had no worries and earning a living was boring. Girls were something you put up with and they spent all their time giggling anyway, so why did he need to earn money?

Then, out of the blue, appeared this funny old man, asking him what his chosen career was going to be. Well, he had to say something, so he said he wanted to be a Wren, because they wore a hat that looked very important, just like an Admiral. That was the end of his careers interview for that day; he was given detention for being cheeky and when he eventually got home his Dad did a bit of butchery practice (without a knife) on his backside for getting a detention.

How unfair life can be!

So, for the next year or so, life carried on as normal for Bob. He took his GCEs and did quite well in most of them and was just drifting towards his 16th birthday and leaving school. But then a very strange thing happened. Bob discovered that girls were not just creatures that giggled all the time; they were real people who knew about things he had not heard of, like knitting, perfume and brassieres. They were different to boys in other ways as well, being an interesting shape, and discovering what made them a different shape became a bit of a challenge. He also found out that kissing could be very different to the wet, sloppy things that Aunty Ethel dished out when she visited. Once you got the hang of it with a girl, kissing was quite enjoyable and sometimes made you feel quite odd. Pleasant, but odd.

But, as time went on, Bob discovered that as well as learning new tricks, like how to undo a brassiere with one hand and eat an ice cream with the other, all in the semi-darkness of a cinema, it cost money to get that girl into the cinema in the first place. In the winter it was the only place you could go with a girl, and cinemas were expensive. Not only that, you were expected to buy them presents and chocolates, all the things Mum had provided in the past.

Big problem… no money!

Bob was now learning that to get the things you enjoy in life you need money and that meant getting a job.

The obvious thing was to become a butcher, so Bob joined his Dad at *Long's The Butchers*, at the grand old age of sixteen. He learnt the skill of dissecting a carcass into chops, steaks and shoulders between visits to the local hospital to have bits of his own body sewn back on, following a succession of nasty accidents with a knife or cleaver. But, like most butchers, Bob soon discovered the other benefits. Women seemed to have an attraction to butchers, for some reason, and his love-life really took off, despite the fact that women's tights were fast becoming the new anti-passion garment.

This interesting and educational part of Bob's life continued for a year or so but, hovering in the distance, was another threat – National Service. When he reached the age of eighteen, Bob would be 'called-up' to join the Army, Air Force or Navy for two years. He would have no choice regarding which service he went into or what he did when he got there.

Now the only boat Bob had been on was the Tilbury Ferry … and he had been seasick. He had been banned from the rifle sideshow at the local fair because he had made a bullet hole in a cuddly toy on the top shelf – and the thought of going anywhere near an aeroplane frightened the life out of him. Maybe the Wrens had not been such a bad idea – after all, they did not go to sea, fire guns or have aeroplanes.

So Bob began to give some serious thought to this National Service business and, like many other lads his age, asked himself the question, 'Do I take pot luck and finish up peeling spuds for two years or volunteer for a bit longer and do something really useful … like marching up and down for three years as a regular soldier?"

He had heard that there were such things as *Conscientious Objectors* but then realised that there had to be a war before you could become one of those, whatever they were.

His mates were full of good suggestions for getting out of National Service: he could develop flat feet, perforate his eardrum or become a monk. None of these appealed to him, even though he was sure he had flat feet. How else could he stand upright without falling over?

Time was getting short and Bob had to make a decision whether to volunteer or not. Being a proud lad, he decided to volunteer so that he could say he had made his own decision on how he would be treated for the next few years. (He was later to learn that the one thing you never do in the Armed Forces is to volunteer for anything.)

'Now, which service should it be?' he pondered. 'Do I want to be constantly seasick, called a "brown job" or a "Brylcreem Boy?' As his Dad had been in the RAF, he chose to volunteer for the Air Force and, as his Mum said, "Blue does suit you dear…"

The decision made, Bob trotted off into town to find the RAF recruiting office. He was greeted by a pleasant young man in a smart blue uniform, who explained how nice the RAF was, how well he would be treated and that he would be a sergeant in no time at all. Now what trade would Bob like to be trained for? He could join the Marine Section to serve on motor boats, the RAF Regiment and learn to march or join the catering section and peel spuds. Oh dear! After long discussions it was decided he would like to train as a Radar Mechanic because, after all, television was the coming thing and the training would be useful, plus of course it did not involve sharp knives and Bob had become quite attached to his fingers.

Bob suddenly became quite popular with all the local girls. He could not understand why but, being a modest sort of chap, he put it down to his natural charm and good looks, although it was probably the thought of having a boyfriend in uniform that attracted them. After all, having a boyfriend away in the forces gave a girl an air of respectability, even if it was false. Despite his new-found popularity, Bob was looking forward to joining up. The rumours he had heard about the Waafs only made him more keen and, after all the things the nice man had said about the RAF, he could not wait to sleep in a nice, warm, centrally-heated room, with plenty of hot water when he wanted a bath. His home for the past 17 years had been very welcoming, but it was so cold in the winter and the old hot water system meant you could only run one bath a day, and that would be in about two inches of hot water.

Before he was accepted into the RAF, however, he had to pass some examinations and have a medical. He took a day off work and made his way to the recruiting and medical centre at the appointed time. Most of the morning was taken up by written exams and interviews with an officer. Having spent an hour or so deciding that *shape A* was the same as *shape* B upside down, that 20 men took twice as long to build a road as 40 men would and that Paris was in France, he went off to lunch with a couple of lads who were also hoping to join the RAF. Their conversation about the Air Force would have had any ex-airman in stitches, especially when they started talking about the accommodation, food and promotion. He would have thought they were describing some luxury hotel.

Lunch over, they returned for the medical examination. They had to go into a room, one by one, for this and were confronted by three men, although there was some doubt in Bob's mind about one of them, especially when this man stared at the lower part of his now naked body and then asked him to cough. The man was obviously not interested in how bad his cough was. Bob had heard about men like him from the boys at school.

Eventually, he was told to put his clothes back on and go into the next room, where a woman in a white coat peered into his ears and eyes and down his throat. She then asked him questions in a very faint whisper while standing behind him. He also had to read from a card on the wall and she finally produced a book that looked like a photograph album.

When she opened the book, each page had a circle on it and this circle was made up of different colour dots, a bit like a dinner plate with a dose of the measles. All a bit confusing, especially when she asked Bob what he could see.

'Ah,' thought Bob, 'this is obviously a catch question,' because all he could see was a circle covered in dots, but as he could not think what the answer should be, he gave the only answer he could think of and said, "A circle made up of coloured dots." The woman was a little surprised by this and Bob thought he had cracked the code. This was obviously an intelligence test and the secret was to tell them what you could see and not to try and double bluff them. She turned the pages and Bob replied with what he saw on each page, which was usually nothing, although sometimes he thought he saw a figure of a dog or a man hidden in the dots.

The medical finally over, all the lads went back into the reception room, everyone discussing what had gone on. One lad described the man that had stared at Bob's nether regions as an 'old queen', but Bob knew better than that. Obviously, this lad would finish up in the Army. Everyone knew that queens were female and wore a crown. In a quiet moment Bob asked the lad next to him how he got on with the intelligence test.

"What intelligence test?" asked the lad.

Bob described the circle of coloured dots and how he was not fooled by it, to which the other chap said, "But that was a colour blindness test. Each circle contained a different number or letter. The woman told me I had got them all right." Although he did not know it at the time, that book of dots was to make a big change in Bob's life.

All that remained now was to sit and wait for the results of his efforts with the entrance exam and the medical.

The RAF must have thought he was bright enough and that he did not have flat feet (whatever they were) because after a week or so he received a letter telling him to report to the Recruiting Centre at 9am in three week's time.

Bob was about to grow up.

2. Welcome to the Air Force

The days before he was due to report were very busy, saying goodbye to all his friends, his girlfriends, the odd aunt and uncle (most of them were odd) and, most importantly, having a haircut. He wanted to look smart and make a good impression so that the nice officers and sergeants would approve of him. Obviously he would need a haircut, so he asked the barber to cut it a bit shorter than usual. Little did he know he had just wasted his money.

Sharp at nine o'clock, he arrived at the Recruiting Office and found he was one of eight new recruits. They were all shapes and sizes, some tall, some short, some fat and some thin and made a very strange-looking bunch. Most of them were only seventeen or eighteen and most were spotty. They were not a bit like Bob's mates and some were quite intimidating, being much taller and obviously very much "men of the world".

He made such a good impression on the nice sergeant that he was put in charge of the party of nine odds and sods, given a railway warrant and told to get them all to the Recruit Reception Unit at Boddington. Off they all ambled to the railway station, complete with their leather-look suitcases full of freshly laundered underpants, thick vests "In case it is cold dear" and packets of biscuits: "You might get hungry on the way". There was one big problem however. Where was Boddington? None of the group knew the answer. One thought it was only just down the road, while someone else thought it was in Wales. Bob decided this was obviously an initiative test the RAF had set him, probably because they thought he was a born leader and would go far in the Air Force. Using all the brainpower he could muster, Bob set about finding a solution to the problem.

Suddenly, he had a flash of inspiration.

"I know... I will ask someone," he said.

The first two people he asked did not seem to know which day it was, so he then asked the man behind the little window in the ticket office.

"Ah," was the reply. "Next train to Charing Cross, then a train from St Pancras."

So began Bob's first grand adventure as an adult – not the snakes and swamps of the jungle, not the frozen wastes of the Arctic, but a simple train journey with the great unknown at the end of it – the London Underground.

They all managed to get off at the right station – it was the end of the line after all – and even managed to find Charing Cross Underground station, even though it was down a backstreet near the river. They were all feeling quite pleased with themselves at this stage; they were all still together and they were not lost... Or were they?

It was decision time again. They studied the Underground maps on the wall and thought how clever they must have been when they built the underground, because all the lines were dead straight, but the problem was, none of the trains went to St Pancras, so once again they decided to ask someone.

The first six people they spoke to did not understand English and all had paper maps of the Underground in their hands and cameras round their necks. Someone said they must be here on holiday, but it was decided that this could not be right because London did not have any beaches.

Eventually they found a native Londoner, who said it was quite simple, "Just get a Northern Line train to Euston and walk from there. St Pancras is only just down the road."

Good. Now they were getting somewhere. They found it quite easy to follow the signs to the Northern Line platforms, but then they had a problem, the tunnel they were walking down split into two, northbound and southbound, but which one did they want?

"Simple," said George. "I was in the scouts and you just follow the sun if you want to go south." But as they were about 40 feet underground they decided that was not such a good idea. They took a vote and decided to head for the southbound platform, after all, people from the North spoke funny and they were sure there would not be any Air Force camps in the north. They were sure they had done the right thing because a sudden breeze came out of the train tunnel and clever George said the wind had been in the north when they left home, so they must be going the right way.

Just then a train emerged from the tunnel.

They settled down on the train and off it went into the tunnel. It soon stopped again at the next station, Waterloo, and off it went again. Bob thought it was quite clever the way the doors only opened on one side of the train and they all opened and closed together.

Meanwhile, George was deep in thought and suddenly said, "We went through Waterloo on the other train. We must be going the wrong way!"

It took another couple of stations to agree that he was right and that they wanted the northbound train after all. Someone even found Euston on the map. So they all got off the train at the next station, crossed over the bridge and got back on the next train going in the opposite direction.

'Piece of cake this Underground lark,' Bob said to himself.

They eventually arrived at Euston and made their way on foot to St Pancras, having asked a rather strangely dressed young lady the way. The lady seemed to be more interested in telling them that she had some friends and they all had rooms nearby than she did giving them instructions, but of course her sales pitch was wasted on this group of innocent 18 year olds.

On the train to Boddington at last, they had time to reflect on the day so far. One lad said he missed his mum already. Two said they would have liked to have met the nice, helpful young lady's friends and the rest were just looking forward to having something to eat. The train finally pulled into Boddington station and they made their way to the exit, where they were met by an airman with an armband with the letters RTO on it. He directed them to an RAF lorry parked outside and told them to get themselves and their luggage on the back of it. George said, with his usual great authority, "I expect the bus has broken down, so they have sent this rather than make us wait." With that, off they went, feeling every single bump through the wooden benches that were fixed along the side and breathing in the exhaust fumes that were sucked into the open back of the truck.

Very soon they drove through the gates of the place that was to be home for most of them for the next two weeks or so. Everything was neat and tidy and the sign said *Welcome to Royal Air Force Boddington*. They got down from the truck and stood in a row outside a building that had a sign saying *Guardroom* and seemed to be full of airmen with white hats.

"I wonder why they have white tops to their hats and white belts?" said Bob. After a general discussion it was decided that it was so they could be seen in the dark, although Harry said he was sure he had heard them called 'snowdrops' but the group did not believe that because the snowdrop is a delicate flower and these chaps did not look too delicate.

Eventually a sergeant with a crown on top of his stripes introduced himself as Flight Sergeant Burton and said he would be looking after them for the rest of the day and showing them where they would be sleeping. He then said that he would "march them down to their billet, to save them walking."

"Obviously," said Bob, "he is making a joke to make us feel at home."

Off they went, with arms and legs going all ways, but none at the same time. Flight Sergeant Burton was trying to make it easy for them by calling out "Left, Right," although none of them knew what this meant. They certainly did not understand the other things he said to himself in his strange accent as they hopped and stumbled their way to their accommodation.

They arrived at a wooden hut with 103 painted in large white numbers on the door. 'This doesn't look too good,' they mumbled to themselves, as Flight Sergeant Burton allocated them a bed each.

"Put your gear away in the lockers and someone will be back in an hour to sign you all in," he said, and marched out of the door.

They took stock of their surroundings. Bob had only visited a hospital once and this place reminded him of the ward his uncle was in, but without any curtains and with a different smell. The hospital smelt of disinfectant, but all he could smell now was stale cigarette smoke and a strange aroma that he learnt later was polish. There were 12 beds down each side of the room with just a bare mattress on them and between each bed was an upright wooden locker that looked a bit like a coffin standing on end and next to that another wooden locker about three feet high and two feet square. These turned out to be a wardrobe and a bedside locker. The floor was covered in brown lino, which had a bit of a shine on it, and the room was lit by about twelve electric light bulbs with white plastic coolie-hat type shades. Bob decided that if you said the room was bare you would be exaggerating.

Evenly placed in the centre of the room were two round, black stoves with black pipes that disappeared up through the ceiling. The stoves were not alight, but a bucket of coke stood beside each one. George was quite upset because, even though they were expected, nobody had made any attempt to light the fires and warm the place up. So everyone set about unpacking their brown cardboard leather-look suitcases and putting their clothes in the lockers.

Suddenly the door crashed open and a loud voice, accompanied by a little man, announced he was Corporal Walker and he was in charge of this hut.

"Today," he said, "you will sign in, be given your eating irons and bedding and I will show you the Airmen's Mess. The rest of the day is yours."

With that, he told them to fall in outside and he would march them to the Orderly Room.

All these strange sayings. Bob's mum was always saying, "Mind you don't fall in" and did an Orderly Room have lots of chairs and tables set out in an orderly fashion?

Off they went. Bob soon began to get the hang of this marching game and realised that you are supposed to swing your arms in the opposite direction to your legs and when you left leg goes forward, your right arm also goes forward. He also worked out that when Corporal Walker said "Left" you put your left leg forward and your right leg went forward when he said "Right". Poor old George was in all sorts of trouble with his left leg and his left arm going forward together and colliding with the man in front of him or behind him.

They eventually arrived at the Orderly Room and Corporal Walker shouted "Halt!"

Now that really *was* a mistake, because nobody knew what to do. The two in front stopped, because they were at the bottom of the steps , but dear old George was at the back and was so busy trying to get everything working at the same time that he did not stop and ploughed into the chap in front of him. Like a set of dominoes, they all went down in a heap at the bottom of the stairs, in full view of the Orderly Room windows. Little Corporal Walker tried to make himself even smaller and wished he could disappear, but his training came to his aid and, in his best stentorian voice, he told them to:

"Sort yourselves out and get in line!"

They then filed into the office where the paperwork they had been given at the Recruiting Office was taken from them. They signed an admission form and were told to report back the next day. In the meantime they would be taken to the Stores to be issued with bedding. In the Stores they were each given four blankets, two sheets, a pillow and pillow case, a white china mug, a knife, fork and desert spoon – and told to take great care of them all as everything was now their responsibility and had to be signed for. Off they then marched, back to the billet. George found this a lot simpler because, with his arms full of blankets, he could not swing them and he only had to concentrate on getting his legs working in the right order.

They dumped their bedding on their chosen beds and sat down to take stock of the situation. One tall, thin lad with spots was complaining bitterly that there was no eiderdown for his bed and he was going to be cold. His mum evidently always put flannelette sheets on his bed in the winter. Now all he had were thick, white objects more like dustsheets than bed-sheets.

With a crash, the door at the end of the room flew open and Corporal Walker marched in.

"Right lads, I will now show you how to make up a Bed Pack and you can spend the rest of the afternoon practising. Every morning you will not leave this hut until your bed pack is made up."

The thought of being shown how to make your bed raised a few smiles, but it became pretty obvious that Corporal Walker did not share the joke and the smiles disappeared rapidly.

"This is how to make a bed pack," continued Corporal Walker, as he laid a blanket on the bed and folded it lengthwise in half and then in half again. He then folded each blanket and sheet so that they were about 24 inches by 18 inches. He then placed a folded blanket in the centre of the first blanket with just one folded edge showing. He then added a sheet, another blanket, a sheet and a final blanket. He wrapped the first blanket round the whole thing, turned it upside down and placed it at the head of the bed with the pillow on top. The whole thing resembled a giant slice of Battenberg cake, topped with a layer of icing.

The room was very quiet, the lads were thinking, with their thoughts ranging from "How do I escape from here" through "surely they have cleaning women to make the beds?" to "Well, that's a bit of a doddle, any fool can do *that*!"

Corporal Walker took his leave with the words, "I want to see all your beds looking like that at 9 o'clock tomorrow morning…"

'At least the RAF starts work at a reasonable time,' thought Bob.

"Oh… and by the way, the Airman's Mess opens at 6.30pm for your supper. Don't forget to take your mug and irons."

Promptly at 6.30 they all made their way to the Airmen's Mess for their "supper", probably expecting to get a sandwich and a glass of Horlicks, but surprise-surprise there was a hot meal waiting for them, accompanied by a mug of tea from the rather battered-looking urn at the end of the counter. What Corporal Walker had described as supper was what they all knew as "tea-time" or, if you were posh, "dinner". But there the similarity stopped, because the two or three choices of hot food bore little resemblance to anything Bob had seen before. Bob ventured to ask the totally bored chap behind the counter what was in one tray and was told "chicken curry, can't you see?" But Bob had no chance of making a visual decision on what to him looked like a cross between brown wallpaper paste and something the cat had done in the corner. He therefore decided to go for the least unappetising offering and finished up with what he believed was toad-in-the-hole, although the holes outnumbered the toads many, many times. Apple pie and custard was on offer for dessert, but they swore the custard was the chicken curry with yellow colouring added.

Half way through the meal an officer and a sergeant came round. The sergeant had an armband on his uniform.

"Any complaints?" asked the sergeant, and Bob was about to open his mouth when the chap next door kicked him hard under the table. All ten people on the table smiled sweetly at the sergeant and said, "No sergeant".

The same drill was performed at each table.

At the end of the meal Bob was rubbing his ankle when his assailant said "You haven't been here long have you? Never complain to the Orderly Officer or sergeant and never volunteer for anything." With that he was gone, saying something about getting to the NAAFI before it closed. The lads from Hut 103 made their way back to the hut and spent the rest of the evening discussing the meal and wondering "If that was supper, what are breakfast and lunch like?"

They were all quite weary by this time and one by one they turned their collection of blankets and sheets into something resembling a bed and eventually someone turned the lights out, but not before they had all got undressed while trying not to let any bare flesh show. One chap even got into bed before he took his trousers off. Then started another whole experience for Bob – the sounds of the night. Not the cry of foxes or other animals, this variety of night sounds was coming from the human beings around him, something he definitely was not used to, as normally he had a bedroom to himself and did not share it with nineteen other humans, each with their own variety of snores, coughs and farts. Someone obviously had a rash, because it sounded as though he was scratching himself continuously and Bob was sure he could hear someone else crying.

After what seemed like a couple of hours sleep Bob was rudely awoken by a horrible rattling and scratching from the wooden box over the door, accompanied by a voice announcing that it was "Reveille". They had decided the previous evening that this box was a loud speaker, but they had no idea what it was used for. Now they knew. Nobody moved out of their bed, they just lay there discussing what should happen next, although they did not have long to wait to find out. With an almighty crash, the door flew open, the Orderly Sergeant from the night before strode in, advising them in an extremely loud voice to remove their hands from a certain part of their anatomy and put their socks on as it was 6.30am and time all good little airmen were out of bed – or words to that effect.

Yet another new experience was now awaiting them, the washing facilities first thing in the morning. A hut of twenty men, but with only six washbasins between them proved a bit of a problem and more than one of them decided to shave at night instead of the morning, something they soon learnt not to do, especially if they had a dark beard. Being polite, Bob waited his turn for a basin and then came yet another new experience: cold water shaving. Bob had been shaving for a year or so but had never had to shave with stone-cold water before. As they stood in the breakfast queue it was quite obvious from all the bits of toilet paper stuck on many faces that he was not the only one.

So here they were, waiting for breakfast and surprise-surprise, so was the chicken curry – this time coloured white and called porridge. The baked beans had a similar appearance but were a slightly different colour and the eggs resembled daisies with a hard yellow centre and frilly bits round the edges. Hunger was getting the better of most of them by this time and the food was eaten in silence. One hero even tried to go back for seconds but returned promptly to the table, followed by a few choice words from the corporal cook describing the lad's parentage. So that was breakfast.

The meal over, they now had to concentrate on turning their sheets and blankets into something called a "Bed Pack", this being the Layer Cake that Corporal Walker had demonstrated yesterday. Eventually, after much discussion and argument, they had all managed to make a "Bed Pack" and were still proudly admiring their creations when Corporal Walker arrived.

He walked slowly down the hut, checking each bed and reaching the end made a little speech, punctuated with a good choice of swearwords that even Bob, a butcher's son, had never heard before. What he was telling them was that they were scruffy, they had not listened to what he had told them and that all their efforts were a complete waste of time. He said he would demonstrate yet again the art of making a bed pack and that for the next hour they would practice this art until each and every one of them could put their blankets and sheets together so that they all looked as though they were in the same Air Force. They would worry about getting the size right tomorrow. He then explained that they would be allocated their uniforms today and he hoped they all knew their sizes (with a strange grin on his face).

"We will march down to the stores to save walking," said Corporal Walker, his hilarious joke raising a titter from the men, this titter turning to groans each and every time they heard this same "joke" over the next few years. They eventually arrived at a long tin shed, with a notice over the door at one end stating that it was *The Clothing Store*. They then had to enter the building in single file and wait to be measured. Down each side of the building were wooden racks stacked with anonymous piles of blue/grey material. In front of each rack was a wooden table and behind each table was a man in a khaki overall coat. Right at the end stood a very elderly, bored-looking man with a tape measure and next to him an even older and even more bored-looking man with a pad and pencil.

"Right you lot," said Corporal Walker. "When I call you forward I want you to start at the end, be measured, and then make your way down the room and back up the other side, by which time you will be a fully equipped airman."

"This is very efficient," said a voice from the back, although most of them were already beginning to realise that things were not what they always seemed in the Royal Air Force.

Then began the slick, efficient and professional issuing of the uniform they would be proud to wear for the next few years. The man with a tape-measure waved the tape up and down their bodies, getting quite close at times; he then wrapped it round their head and glanced at their feet, all the time calling out numbers in a totally bored voice. His granddad next to him was writing these numbers down on a piece of paper, which he then gave to each person with the instruction to show it at each table.

At the first table Bob was given "One kitbag, Airman". At the next he received "One webbing set, Airman" and so on, until eventually he came to the actual clothing section and started with "Four knickers, Airman" and "Four vests, Airman", then followed "shorts, gymnastic", "socks, blue" and so on.

The interesting bit was reaching the uniform issue.

The man at the table would call out "32 waist, 34 leg" from the piece of paper and a voice would come from behind him, "No 32 waist left; give him 36." This happened a number of times before Bob reached the end table, by which time he had a pile of clothing, boots, shoes, and a wonderful small white cotton pouch known as "A housewife" whatever that was.

They were all then marched back to their hut, told to put on their 'working blue' and boots and report outside in 30 minutes, carrying their 'best blue' and shoes, for a visit to the tailor. They discovered that the 'working blue' was, in fact, the battledress top and trousers with belt loops, with the 'best blue' being the jacket with shiny buttons and the trousers that needed braces to hold them up.

They all struggled into their working blue and without exception they all had problems with the shirts. These were made of a thick material and did not have collars, the collars being separate and held onto the shirt with two little things called "collar studs", which were of different shapes, with one having a swivel end to make it easier to push through the hole in the shirt and collar.

"You will grow into it lad."

Some of Bob's new companions had obviously only just learnt to tie their own shoelaces, so attaching the collar and then knotting the tie was quite a challenge for them, but, eventually, they all managed to assemble the various bits and pieces of uniform into something vaguely resembling an airman and waited outside for Corporal Walker.

When he arrived it was obvious that he was doing his best not to laugh at the sight that met him. Most had tried to put their new berets on and the sight of a bunch of skinny youths with berets flat as pancakes on their heads made them look more like a parade of drawing pins than a potential fighting force.

A fine body of men, destined to be a superior fighting machine.

They were eventually marched down to the hut marked "Tailor's Shop" and, whatever they were expecting, Saville

Row it was not, just three men with tape-measures, each holding what looked like a white, overgrown peppermint, which, they were later to find out, was a piece of chalk. Each airman then stood in front of one of the chalk-wielders. There was a great deal of tut-tutting, mumbled words like "hopeless" and "do they think we can do *anything* with these" and then great stripes of chalk were put all over the jackets and trousers until they resembled a dyslexic zebra.

The *working blues* were then replaced by the *best blues* and the process was repeated, at the end of which both uniforms had the wearer's name written in chalk on the back and were hung on a rack behind the three men. Each of the lads was then given a pair of brown overalls to wear. These, they found out, were called "denims".

Everyone was then told to report back to the Tailor's Shop later the next day to collect their freshly tailored uniform. When they eventually went back to the Tailor's Shop they were presented with a very pleasant surprise; gone were the baggy trousers that would look good on a clown, gone were the jackets designed to fit Billy Bunter and in their place were uniforms that more or less fitted and were quite smart, even though the cloth did resemble a hairy blanket. They could not wait to get back to their hut, put everything on and have a good look in the mirror. They even felt a bit proud, but of course they would never admit it to each other.

There then followed days of stamping and marking, nothing to do with drill movements but all to do with their new identity – their Service Number. Bob was to be introduced to a seven digit number that, although he did not know it at the time, would be engraved in his memory for the rest of his life. He was no longer a person, he was a number. They were given a set of metal stamps and told to stamp their new number on their "irons" (their knife, fork and spoon) and using marking ink and a pen they had to mark EVERY piece of their equipment, every sock, their tie, beret, even that strange item, the "housewife".

Next they learnt the art of turning that pancake of a beret into something that resembled a real hat instead of something that French onion sellers wore. They learnt that RAF berets were always too big, something Bob could not understand, why not make them smaller and save material? They were probably made in France, he decided, but then realised they were issuing oversized uniforms to everyone, which then had to be reduced by the tailors. This was obviously a devious plan to fool the enemy into thinking all airmen were over 6 feet tall with 44 inch chests and big heads.

So while the tailors had sorted out the coats and jackets, the lads had to adapt the headwear to match the requirements of the RAF themselves and learnt, by fair means and foul, the art of shrinking the beret and customising the peaked "best blue" hat, although they were warned not to touch the peaked cap until after basic training. They learnt that if you put a woollen article into very hot water and then straight into cold water it will shrink; something their mothers had known for years, no doubt, and now something every Airman knew. So for hours each evening they would fight over the limited supply of hot water in an attempt to reduce the diameter of their pancake and then walk around with a wet hat on their head so that it would dry in the right shape. Their mothers would have had a fit and said, "You'll catch your death of cold!" Eventually they all had something that resembled a RAF beret, although some were better than others. Throughout his career, Bob noticed there was always someone that resembled an offset mushroom.

They all knew what the peaked caps of the American airmen looked like and everyone wanted to adopt that style, but of course the RAF peaked cap had a top that was completely circular, rigid and lacking any shape, the peak stuck out almost at right-angles. They learnt that you could remove the stiffening wire in the top, or bend it to your own shape and you could "slash" the peak. This involved cutting the stitching at each end of the peak and changing the angle so that you looked more like a Guardsman and less like a penguin. They were warned not to alter this hat at all unless they wanted to be on a "fizzer", which they learnt was slang for a "charge" which resembled being on detention at school – plus hard labour.

They now had something resembling a smart uniform, although Bob noticed that although all the uniforms were to the same standard, once they were placed on certain people the brand new, pressed and shiny outfit took on a whole new life. In one case, Tubby Franklin, it assumed the personality of a large sack of potatoes. Corporal Walker had spent some time showing them where everything went, which jacket went with which trousers and how to wear the hats.

"Watch this lads," he said. "Your leather edge on your beret should be level and one inch above your eyebrows."

This was a problem for one poor lad whose eyebrows were desperately trying to make contact with his hairline.

"The badge should be over your left eye and the spare material pulled down over the right ear."

This really was a challenge, because, as Bob was to discover constantly over the coming weeks, left and right are a problem to a lot of Airmen! Eventually, with a lot of pulling, stretching, cursing and crying, Corporal Walker was satisfied that their appearance was of a standard that would not frighten the outside world and he announced that a local photographer (probably his uncle) would be coming to camp the next day if anyone wanted their photograph taken in their "smart" new uniform. The next day you would have been hard pushed to find more preening and mirror gazing at a Miss World contest, everyone wanting a photograph to send to their mums, girlfriends, someone else's girlfriend or anybody remotely interested in this latest fine example of a defender of the realm.

Corporal Walker explained to them that they were nearing the end of their stay at the camp. They would be having a medical – "to make sure our bodies can stand the weight of the uniform," thought Bob – an interview to finalise the job they would be trained for and then they would be off to their basic training for six weeks, something that would really turn them into a strong, fit, fighting force. Bob looked around at his new friends – and wondered.

The next day they had to go to the camp cinema to watch a film about "the dangers of life as an airman". They all had a discussion as to what it was all about.

"I know," said Barry. "It will be about guns and bullets and things." Someone else said they hoped it would be about aircraft crashes and things like that, but nobody really knew what was in store. They settled down in their seats and the picture of a pretty girl appeared on the screen, well dressed and looking decidedly non-dangerous. The soundtrack then went on to describe this girl as one of the biggest dangers to the modern airman. Then followed an hour of full colour, graphic pictures of a variety of human "bits" that had been attacked by various sexual diseases. Not a sound came from the audience as the soundtrack warned of the dangers of "not taking precautions" and what to look for if you thought you might have caught something. Half the audience were already scratching themselves, the other half were swearing a silent oath never to go near a woman again. When they got out into the daylight at the end of the film it was obvious that green skin does not go well with Air Force blue and it was only a few with strong stomachs that made it to the mess for their meal.

Before they were finally sent off to their Initial Training, or "square-bashing" as they were told it was called, they had to decide what trade they wanted to follow in their new career in the Royal Air Force. As they soon found out, the decision was not really theirs as they were only given a choice of three or four "trades", the choice having no connection with their background or anything they had requested at their recruiting interview. Anything with a bit of interest or skill attached to it required them to sign on for at least five years. Sign on for nine years and the choice was limitless. So Bob was given the option of becoming a Stores Assistant or Catering Assistant, which, as he had no desire to run a corner shop or learn how to peel spuds, he declined. However, sign on for five years and he was told he could be a Radar Mechanic, Clerk, Policeman or Engine Mechanic.

With due consideration he decided that it would be a good idea to be a Radar Mechanic and then he could mend television sets in his spare time.

"Sorry lad," said the interviewer. "Your colour vision is not good enough because of all the coloured wires." Obviously Bob's problem with the coloured dots on his medical was now public knowledge and part of his Personal Record. He did not fancy being a pen-pusher or a copper (a "Snowdrop" as he had heard them called), so Engine Mechanic it would be.

Now the nearest Bob had been to an aircraft was on Battle of Britain Day at his local airfield, when he had stood in the crowd and watched Spitfires doing rolls and loops in the sky. He did not have a clue how an engine worked, especially the ones without propellers, but it sounded interesting.

So now they were all set up with their new trades, they had their smart new uniforms and they even knew how to make a bed-pack. They all stood proudly in their best blue for their photographs and the discussions in the hut at night were based on how interesting it all was now that they were real airmen.

Little did they know what was in store as they waited with their kitbags the next morning to board the transport that would take them on to their next camp.

Their transport turned out to be quite ancient-looking open lorries with canvas covers over the back, with the rear of this cover open to the road. Having managed to scramble into the back without taking the skin off his shins, Bob found that the seats ran the length of the truck and were simple wooden planks with no back-rest. When everyone had managed to get themselves and their kit bags, small packs, large packs, ammunition pouches and all the other odd shaped items, loosely known as their "kit" on board, they set off for their new home. Bob thought the corporal had said it was Bridgeford, although he had a strange smile on his face when he said it.

The journey was cold (it was January), bumpy, noisy and very smelly. The open back sucked in the fumes from the exhaust and the sickly petrol fumes made everyone feel very queasy and they all said they would be glad when they arrived.

Little did they know...

The joys of Fire Picket.

"The charge is 'misuse of an Airman's groundsheet'…"

3. Corporal Punishment

"My name is Corporal Jones. You address me as 'Corporal' and stand to attention at all times when you speak to me. Is that clear?" Not a murmur from the truckload of raw recruits just arrived from Boddington. "Just my bloody luck, a load of bleedin' deaf mutes!" said the short, fat man with razor-sharp creases in his trousers and toecaps that looked as though they were made of black glass. "I will try again. You will just have to lip-read." He repeated his opening gambit and this time a sound more like a strangled frog than a roaring lion came from the assembled recruits, most of whom had suddenly lost all the colour from their faces.

So this was Wednesford!

After a third attempt he seemed to be happy with the response and told them he would march them to their hut, they would have five minutes to stow their kit and fall in outside. The new arrivals were lined up in three rows at this stage and in a voice that would do justice to a ships siren he shouted "left turn". At which they all shuffled to the left – except one poor soul in the front row who turned to the right. A silence even more silent than the silence that went before fell over the assembled shambles.

"What is your name lad?"

"James."

"James *what*?"

"James Clark."

This was obviously not going very well. Corporal Jones's face was getting redder by the minute while Jimmy Clark resembled a milk jelly, all white and wobbly. Eventually Jimmy remembered that he had to call the little fat gentleman "Corporal" and "Left turn" meant exactly what it said on the tin.

They found themselves in a hut that looked exactly like the one they had just left at Boddington, the beds looked the same, so did the furniture and the coke fires. There were two main differences that were most obvious; the floor had lino that was so shiny it looked wet and the stove was jet black and the brick hearth was a brilliant white.

They all chose a bed and dumped their "kit" on the bare springs – not so much springs as plain wire set out in two inch squares. Jim thought he would be clever; do not have a bed near the door, he had learnt already that those near the door got all the rotten jobs, and to be near the fire for warmth. This turned out to be a mistake though as everyone sat on his bed to keep warm in the evenings, making his "area" in a mess and preventing him getting into bed.

Having claimed their beds and unloaded their kit, everyone gathered outside the hut to wait for Corporal Jones who said he would take them to the Mess for their evening meal. Eventually they arrived at the Airmans Mess, having had a five minute march that included a good number of references by Corporal Jones to their sex, their parentage and comments on their brain power. The meal turned out to be a real surprise; their meals at Boddington had looked like something familiar but had tasted completely different, Bridgeford had gone one better – the meal looked like nothing they recognised and tasted even less familiar. When Bob asked someone behind the counter what the undefined lumps in the strange colour gravy were, the answer was "s___t", obviously a man that was proud of his work. They were all glad to eat something however and having washed their mug and "irons" in a tank full of slightly warm, greasy water they walked back to their hut making bets on just what it was they had just eaten. Corporal Jones had told them that reveille was at 06.30 and they had to parade outside the hut sharp at 07.00 and he would march them to breakfast, although Bob wondered why they gave the meals different names if they were all going to look and taste the same. They sat around talking for an hour or so and one by one they turned in, having had what they thought was a hard day – little did they know just what a hard day really was.

The silly so-and-so has dropped his irons again!

Sharp at 06.30 the tannoy crackled and announced that it was time to start a new day. For a while nobody stirred – until the door burst open and a corporal invited them to get out of their pits, slip along to the nice warm bathroom and get themselves smart and ready for Corporal Jones at 7 o'clock, Bob could not remember the corporal's exact words, but he got the message. Suddenly there was a mad rush for the hut next door that had "ablutions" written on it. This is where Bob learned important lesson number one; when 40 half-asleep airmen descend on 20 wash basins, equipped with about 10 semi-opaque mirrors, it is every man for himself especially when you only have cold water to shave in and none of the basins have plugs, the chains were there but not the plugs. Bob made a mental note to "obtain" a plug as soon as possible and then guard it with his life.

Eventually every one was back in the hut and had managed to assemble their clothing into what they thought was correct for the smart airmen they surely were. It was soon apparent that their idea of smart was somewhat different to Corporal Jones' view, having lined them up outside the hut he proceeded to carry out an inspection. John White was standing next to Bob and when Corporal Jones arrived in front of him he stopped and stared.

"What is your name airman?"

John remembered all that had gone before and correctly answered, "White, Corporal."

"Did you shave this morning, White?"

"Yes Corporal," said John.

"Then next time stand closer to the bloody razor! Go back and shave again and be back here in seven minutes or you will miss breakfast," said Corporal Jones, who then carried on inspecting everyone else.

He pronounced that we were the dirtiest, scruffiest and thickest new intake that he had ever had. He would march us to breakfast and would then spend the rest of the day trying to teach us how to be real human beings, although he thought that would probably be an impossible task.

After another anonymous meal, this time called breakfast, we all assembled outside our hut, waiting for Corporal Jones to enlighten us with his views of how a real human being should look and behave. The morning was spent on the parade ground with Corporal Jones explaining how he expected his "Flight" – C Flight, Intake 134, hut 27 – as we were now known, to dress and behave.

Half way through the morning a brown Morris van pulled up at the side of the parade ground and a shutter opened at the side.

"Right lads," said Corporal Jones. "That is the NAAFI van; you can have 10 minutes break."

C Flight then walked quietly to the van, formed an orderly queue and politely asked the girl serving them for "A cup of tea please". This was their introduction to the NAAFI, the NAAFI girls and the life-saving liquid they called tea. Today's politeness and orderly behaviour would bear no resemblance to events in the future.

The NAAFI break over, Corporal Jones formed them up into three ranks and said he would now start them on the road to becoming drill experts. He explained that if he said "By the left quick march," it meant they would be marching two or three abreast and they should line themselves up on the person on their left, but if he said "Left, right" while they were marching, it meant you put your left or right leg forward in time to his instructions.

So off they went across the square, in time to Corporal Jones "Left, right…" Bob was feeling quite proud of the fact that he was marching in time with everyone else.

Suddenly a voice bellowed in his ear.

"Wilson! When you swing your left leg forward, you should also swing your right arm forward not your left arm."

Corporal Jones promptly brought the flight to a halt and proceeded to demonstrate the correct sequence of events. Having done that, he then invited Bob to demonstrate his method of marching – and the flight promptly fell about laughing. There followed a lengthy lesson for Bob until he finally mastered the simple task of swinging your left arm forward at the same time as your right leg.

Important lesson number two.

In the afternoon they learnt how to lay all their kit out on their beds for a "kit inspection". Kit Inspections were frequent events, they were told, and usually followed a "bull-night". Evidently bull nights were held once a week and were followed by an officer's inspection of the hut and ablutions the following morning. There was a complicated and unnecessary (Bob thought) way of laying all your kit out, right down to your toothbrush and razor and a photograph of this layout was pinned on the noticeboard. They were told that tonight was bull night and that everything in the hut had to be washed, dusted and polished. A Senior Man (Harry Sharp) was appointed for the hut and he was told to organise everyone into their own task.

They were shown where to find the polish, etc, and introduced to the "bumper", this being a heavy, square lump of metal attached to a long handle by a swivel. The face of the "bumper" consisted of a polishing cloth. After putting polish on the floor, the bumper was slid backwards and forwards to shine the floor. In the cupboard, with the bumper, they found a number of pieces of thick felt; these were oblong and just about the size of a foot. A debate then started about their purpose, someone thought they were table mats to stand your pint pot on when it was full of hot tea from the Naafi, but that theory was soon shouted down when they realised that Naafi tea was never that hot. Brian Gibson had been in the ATC however and was able to explain that these were called "Pads", the idea being that you scrounged some packing felt from the stores, cut it into shoe-sized pieces and then used them to skate across the polished floor. Someone suggested a game of ice hockey might be a good idea, but Brian explained the idea was that the pads were kept by the door and when you came in with your studded boots on you slid on two of these pads to your bed-space, where you promptly removed your boots. This had two purposes, it prevented your boots scratching the polished floor and it polished the floor at the same time. Harry Sharp, the Senior Man then said that no-one would be allowed into the hut without using these pads and should anyone see someone ignoring this rule they should shout "pads" and a suitable job would be given to the culprit on bull-night.

So started their first bull-night. To an onlooker the sight of 20 or so housewife virgins trying to clean, polish and dust the furniture and ablutions would have been hilarious. Bob himself was given the job of cleaning the three baths in the ablution hut and he spent an hour trying to remove a brown stain that ran from the cold tap. But it was rust and he would never be able to clean it. Likewise Dusty Miller spent ages trying to clean the mirrors until he realised the haze was a normal feature of RAF mirrors. Brian Gibson, being ex ATC and an "old hand", proved to be full of useful hints and made himself a lot of friends that night. With his help they just about managed to finish their jobs before lights-out, having spent almost six hours doing what their Mum would probably have done in two hours on her own.

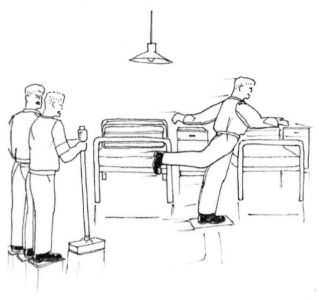

"He used to be a ballet dancer."

Following what they now accepted as being breakfast, they were instructed to stand by their bed space and wait for the hut inspection. Eventually Corporal Jones appeared in the doorway and shouted "Attention, officer present!" He and the officer then inspected each bed space, checking under the bed, the bedpack, and wiping their fingers along ledges, door frames and the top of wardrobes. Harry Sharp was told to accompany them.

Faults were found with almost every bed space and these were pointed out to Harry. The officer nearly burst a blood vessel when he found specks of coal dust on the white fire hearth and demanded to know who was responsible for cleaning the stove area. Corporal Jones was then told to give Tommy Davis extra fatigues. When the officer left the hut

Corporal Jones returned and took great delight in telling them they had to do it all over again ready for a further inspection the next morning, so yet again they had to spend the evening on "bull". But at least they had some idea what to expect from an inspection and they had already learnt some shortcuts and the phrase "bullshit baffles brains" was beginning to make sense. But at the same time they were beginning to wonder if this way of life was normal in the Royal Air Force and were they going to be glorified housewives for the rest of their service.

This was probably the time when calendars started to appear on the back of wardrobe doors, with a running total of "days to do" marked clearly. They probably did not realise it, but they were also beginning to bond with each other and become a team. Nicknames started to appear, some of which are unrepeatable, some being quite apt and funny and others which were derogatory and probably amounted to bullying.

The inspection went off without too many problems and C Flight was then marched to the camp cinema for an 'educational film'. Expecting to be shown a film about aircraft, guns and drill, they were quite surprised when the film started with a nurse on the screen who announced that they were about to learn about the dangers of being a young man in the 1950s. 'What could she mean?' they wondered.

Brian, whose uncle was a doctor, whispered to Bob, "This will be about keeping yourself clean, washing your hands and what do if you catch the flu."

He was partly right, because the film showed, in graphic detail, how important it was to mix in the right company and how to keep yourself clean, although the body parts being scrubbed were not hands but much more private parts of the male anatomy – and it was not flu that was being caught but complaints that did strange and horribly unsightly things to those private parts.

Because the film was in glorious colour and was not hampered by an "X" certificate, the sounds that came from the audience were not those that would normally come from an all-male audience watching a film with girls in it. The sounds were more akin to watching a film of a lion attacking and eating a deer. After the 45-minute film show, the general consensus was that the human race would cease to expand if they had anything to do with it.

"The VD film usually puts them off for a few days."

When they got back to their hut, Corporal Jones told them that tomorrow morning they would be having an "F.F.I. Inspection" but would not tell them what F.F.I. stood for, so after their evening meal there was a lively debate on just what the letters were an abbreviation for – was it Flat Feet Inspection? Fat Finger Inspection? Someone even suggested it might be a competition to find the Funniest Face. No one knew, so they went to bed happy.

"Silly *#!*!\$, that was only the swab!"

Following yet another hearty breakfast they were marched down to the medical centre, by now having decided that this was going to be a Flat Feet Inspection – that is, until they were told to remove their trousers and "drawers, Airmen" and line up by the door in the corner. It was quite a cold day and there were a number of giggles and sly glances along the queue. Eventually the door opened. Inside the room were two low benches parallel to each other, about 30 inches apart. An officer with a metal cane was standing to one side, at the end of the benches.

"Right airmen," said Corporal Jones. "You are to form up on the benches with one foot on each bench. When you get to the end, the officer will instruct you."

They shuffled along the bench, with everything swinging in the breeze, until they were face-to-face with the officer, who then proceeded to take the weight off their 'meat and two veg' with his metal cane while carrying out a study of these most private parts. He then moved behind them and instructed them to bend down and touch their toes while he repeated the exercise from the rear.

They returned to the other room and dressed, having got to know their room-mates very intimately indeed. Someone joked that when the officer was in the Officers Mess that evening and someone asked him what he had been doing that day he would probably say that he had "looked up an old friend". When Corporal Jones formed them up ready to march back to the hut he asked them how they had enjoyed their "Free From Infection" examination.

So that is what F.F.I. stood for!

The next week or so was spent perfecting their drill techniques and learning that left means left and right means right. They also learnt that you do not have to look where you are going when you are marching, being given the "eyes left" instruction while marching straight ahead meant you had to keep marching in a straight line but turn your head as far as you could to the left to look at an imaginary person standing beside the marching column. This led to a number of strange incidents initially, but they soon got the hang of it, except for Taffy Jones, who had a problem co-ordinating most of his limbs. He even had a problem getting his left leg to go forward at the same time as everyone else's and his *eyes right* seemed to be in a totally different direction altogether. When the order was given to "Left turn" or "Halt", guess who turned right or marched on into the airman in front of him? Taffy Jones. The strange thing was that Corporal Jones never seemed to shout at him or question his parentage in the same way he did to the rest of the Flight.

The lads were feeling quite pleased with their progress, but then Corporal Jones informed them that they were going to the Armoury to collect their rifles, which promptly divided them into two schools of thought, those who were dreading the thought and those who just could not wait to get their hands on a real weapon. There was one common thought, however – keep Taffy away from guns for as long as possible!

They need not have worried, because the old Lee Enfield .303 rifles they were issued with had less chance of firing a real bullet than Taffy did of getting his feet to work in the right sequence. The rifles had obviously been cleaned and polished by the few hundred recruits that had looked after them for their six weeks training, but if anyone attempted to fire one they would be more likely to kill themselves than the person they were aiming at. These rifles were just one stage up from the pitchforks used by the Home Guard.

So, just when they thought they had cracked this drill business, an extremely heavy and awkward piece of kit was added to the equation. Not only did you have to get your feet doing the right thing but you also had to try to remember to move the rifle in the right general direction at the same time, without poking the person behind you in the eye or knocking your neighbour's hat off. Shouted orders such as "Order Arms" or "Present Arms" entered their vocabulary and they learnt which foot went in front of the other one when instructed to "Present Arms". Poor Taffy had great problems with this manoeuvre, however, and only managed to stay upright twice out of nine attempts.

Most of their evenings were spent polishing their boots, the floor or their rifles, although they might creep across to the Naafi for a sixpenny glass of orange squash and a quick chat-up of the Naafi girls. Once they found out the airman's version of what the letters NAAFI stood for, however, they soon realised the same meaning applied to most of the Naafi girls (No ambition and flip-all interest – or words to that effect) and chatting the girls up began to feature less and less in their spare time activities.

"I think what she is telling you to do is physically impossible anyway."

Now and again, when they had some money to spare, they would venture to the camp cinema for an evening of enlightenment. *The Astra,* as it was known, was manned by airmen from the camp and showed films that were a few years old and most definitely not picked for an audience of sex-starved young men.

"Being nearly Pay Day, at least we can get a decent seat."

The sound effects and commentary provided by the audience during love scenes would have turned John Wayne's wig grey and it was not unusual for a tense silence during a particularly sad scene to be broken, very loudly, by the after-effects of the baked beans they had had for lunch. Because all the staff were from the camp, including the projectionist, the continuity sometimes went astray and, on a number of occasions, the leading man would be shot and buried, only to reappear twenty minutes later, completely fit and well. Good old Enoch had got the reels mixed up again!

Their days on the square were beginning to pay off and on most days their communal arms and legs managed to move more or less in time with each other and in the same general direction. Even their arms drill was quite co-ordinated, with the response to the "Order Arms" command sounding more like a rough motor bike than the long round of applause that it had mimicked in the early days. Even complicated manoeuvres like "right wheel" and "about turn" were mastered.

One Bull Night everyone was busy on their allocated task and Ginger was in great voice with his version of *Mr Sandman* helping his efforts with the "bumper". Long swings of the heavy bumper were accompanied by his stentorian "Mr Sandman, send me a dream…" and he was obviously wrapped up in his work. So wrapped up that he did not hear the shout "officer present" or notice everyone else in the hut dropping what they were doing and springing to attention.

So there was Ginger, putting on a private performance of his repertoire in the centre of the hut for the Duty Officer's benefit. It was obvious that the dressing down he received was delivered with a slight smile on the officers lips.

The lads had now been at Wednesford for a few weeks and their first long weekend pass was not too far off. Coaches were to be laid on to Manchester, Birmingham and London and free railway warrants given out. Everyone was to travel in their best blues and they were warned of the dire consequences should they be late back…

4. Preparing to Pass Out

After a long journey home, Bob arrived at the Wilson family flat above the butcher's shop, feeling very proud in his best blue, peaked cap and highly-polished shoes. His Dad was his normal non-committal self and said, "You look well lad. When do you go back?" His Mum, on the other hand, could hardly hide her tears of pride when she saw her little boy, now all grown up and looking very smart in his nice blue uniform.

His Mum had cooked him a special meal and invited some of his old friends round to join them. Bob then spent the evening answering all their questions about life in the RAF, such as, "Have you flown an aeroplane yet?"

"Do they give you nice meals?" was his Mum's concern and she also wanted to know if the maids changed their bedclothes frequently. After an exhausting evening of questions, which Bob tried to answer truthfully, but with the odd word like "kite" and " the aircraft driver" added for effect, he went to bed in the luxury of a room to himself with no-one to keep him awake with their snoring, burping or passing of wind.

The next evening Bob was invited to his cousin Joan's 21st birthday party in the back room of the Working Men's Club. He seemed to be the star attraction, especially among the girls, because everyone was coming up to him and asking the usual questions: Had he flown yet? Was he an officer? And of course, "When do you go back?" The latter question was from the lads, who were obviously envious and couldn't wait to get the full attention of the local girls again. Bob revelled in this new found attention from the opposite sex and felt ten feet tall, until Uncle Jim, who was acting as MC for the evening, asked them to form a large circle. He then said everyone should get to know each other by turning to the person on their left and shaking hands. Everyone turned left, as suggested by Uncle Jim, except, of course, Bob, who managed to turn to his right. The resulting cheer was accompanied by a rapid change of colour to Bob's face and the feeling that he had instantly lost at least two feet in height. The rest of the evening was spent hiding behind a pint glass!

The following day Bob was paraded round to all the relations and friends that had not been at the previous night's party and he spent most of the day answering the usual questions. By mid-afternoon it was all beginning to wear a bit thin and Bob was actually starting to wish he was back at Stalag Wednesford. After tea his Dad drove him to the station for what Bob was about to experience – Sunday evening travel, courtesy of British Railways. He had to change in London, which required going from Victoria to Euston to get his train north and, although his train to Victoria was twenty minutes late arriving in Victoria, Bob had plenty of time to get to Euston and decided to walk. He soon found that walking through that part of London in RAF uniform was not the most sensible thing to do. He lost count of the times a shadowy figure stepped out of a doorway and offered him "a good time". They were mostly reasonably smartly dressed, with short skirts and tight jumpers, although those with beards were more conservative in their attire!

He managed to arrive in Euston in one piece, but a lot wiser as to what certain words and phrases really meant when used in a selling context. The first thing he discovered was that his train was to be leaving 45 minutes late, due to the non availability of an engine (a basic requirement, thought Bob). This concerned him a bit because the train was due into Lichfield at 10.00pm and the last transport was due to leave for the camp at 11.00pm. This only gave him 15 minutes at Lichfield to catch the truck back to camp.

Eventually, British Railways found an engine from somewhere and off they went, non-stop to Birmingham, next stop Lichfield... or so they thought. The first thing Bob noticed was that a window had it leather strap missing and that it was jammed in the open position, this together with the non-existent heating, which he knew to be normal, made him wonder if he should move compartments. However the train was very full, with people standing in the corridor, so he decided to sit tight.

After about 15 minutes, the train stopped in the middle of nowhere, with no lights visible to give them a clue as to their whereabouts. Then a figure with a lamp appeared, walking down the track alongside the train. Shortly afterwards he re-appeared on Bob's side, walking back towards the engine. Someone stuck their head out of the open window and asked what was going on. The voice with the lamp said, "Someone has reported seeing sparks coming from under the train and we are just checking." Shortly after that, the train started to move, accompanied by a loud cheer, but the joy was short-lived because they stopped at the next station and the whole inspection procedure was repeated, using the dim lights from the station.

By this time, the natives were becoming restless, especially the ones in Bob's compartment. Eventually the train moved again, but only to stop at the next, much larger, station. Station staff walked down the platform, announcing that, as the train was now so late, it would be the last train of the day and would therefore stop at all stations to Birmingham!

By this time it was fast approaching 10.45pm and Bob was panicking. His pass expired at 23.59 and he knew there was no chance he would even be at Birmingham by this time.

Eventually the train crawled into Lichfield at around one o'clock in the morning. The station was deserted, apart from six or seven people getting off the train. Big decision time; what could he do now? Fortunately, three of the alighting passengers were also in uniform and obviously from the camp and they formed an instant debating society to decide what to do. Someone suggested they should get a porter or some other railway worker to sign something to prove their train was late. They could find no-one, although they suspected the only British Railways employee had locked himself in the ladies toilet.

So now, how could they get the 15 miles back to camp? Someone found the phone number of a local taxi company scribbled in the phone box and they decided to give them a try, but had they got enough money? Between them they had five shillings and some coppers for the phone and they dialled the number. An obviously just-woken-up voice answered and agreed to take them to the camp after much pleading and arguing, with money not being mentioned. Eventually, a battered Austin 16 turned up, with the driver wearing a duffle coat over his pyjamas.

"It will cost you seven and six lads," he informed them.

Oh dear! Not to be beaten, they said to him, "You can either go back to bed, having had a completely wasted journey, or you can take us and earn five bob, which is all we own between us." Fortunately, he had been in the RAF and felt sorry for them, although in truth he probably felt it would give his wife more time to cool down after being woken by the phone in the middle of the night.

So finally, at 1.40am, the three weary travellers arrived back at RAF Wednesford – and were promptly put on a charge. This, for the uninitiated, means that you have to appear in front of a senior officer and answer the charge that you have broken the rules – in Bob's case the charge was being absent without leave (AWOL). Later the next day he was marched in front of the officer and told to remove his hat. (Evidently this was to prevent the prisoner hitting the officer with his hat!) He was given the minimum opportunity to speak in his defence and the officer pronounced his verdict.

"Guilty as charged, and his punishment, seven days restriction of privileges." He was then instructed to replace his hat and was quick-marched out of the room.

Once outside, he was told to report to the Guardroom at 6.00pm that evening and every evening for the next seven days. He was instructed that he should be in his "best blue" and that he should be immaculate. For the rest of the day Bob carried on with the normal daily activities of "Left turn, right turn, halt, about turn," etc, etc. At 6 o'clock sharp Bob joined a handful of other "sinners" outside the guardroom. Most of them were "sprogs" like Bob, but a couple of older lads were obviously old hands at "jankers" and they knew just what to expect. They were quite cheerful and said it was because Sgt Saxby, who would normally carry out their inspection and allocate their punishment, was on leave and in his place was Sgt Peacock. Sgt Peacock, they announced, was "demob happy". He had just completed 22 years service and was due to leave the Service at the end of the following week.

However, the 'old lags' appeared to be completely wrong in their assessment, because Sgt Peacock proceeded to pull them all to pieces for being scruffy, dirty and a disgrace to the RAF when they formed up in front of the Guardroom. But he then marched them to one side, out of sight of the Guardroom, whereupon it became obvious that he had just been putting on a display for the benefit of the Snowdrops. He allocated jobs that were simple tasks, like filling coal buckets or sweeping an already swept pavement. Bob was sure Sgt Peacock and the two older lads then disappeared round the back of the E.T. room for a crafty smoke. Bob had wondered what just what "E.T." stood for and had looked inside the small room. Inside was a washbasin and a shelf, with a collection of bottles and containers on it. Bob was none the wiser.

The dull routine of marching, bull nights and kit inspections carried on each day, but the odd more interesting film or lecture was being introduced. One morning they were marched to the Education Section for a lecture on looking after the Queen's property, namely the airman's body. The Pilot Officer lecturer told them that if they spent too long sunbathing and then went sick with sunburn or sunstroke, they would be charged with wasting time on a self-inflicted injury. They learnt how to keep themselves clean when water was in short supply and how to avoid strange illness when in the tropics. The lecturer then moved on to personal relationships both with the same sex as well as the opposite sex. It was pointed out that any same-sex relationship was strictly forbidden and would result in severe disciplinary action. Relationships with the opposite sex would not be treated in the same way – as long as you were not caught practising on RAF property.

The officer then moved on to how to look after your equipment – especially the personal bits that were involved in relationships with the opposite sex – and asked if we had all seen the sex education film. The response to his question was very mixed! Bob was very interested in the next topic, the ET Room, and was to look on the room in a totally different light from now on. They were shown, with very graphic diagrams, which bits were at risk and how to keep them clean, which was where the ET Room came in. The idea was that if you had been in town for the evening and had "tasted the fruits", as he delicately put it, on your way back you should call in at the ET Room, which was usually behind the Guardroom, and thoroughly wash the active bits and treat them with the various creams and potions supplied.

E.T. stood for *Early Treatment*.

The Pilot Officer asked if there were any questions at the end of the session, but everyone was strangely quiet. However, Tommy Davis asked if it was true that bromide was added to the mess tea, because when he was home on leave he felt things were not working properly when he was with his girlfriend. The lecturer gave a very evasive answer, saying that perhaps Tommy's taste in women had become more sophisticated now that he was an airman! So the rumours about bromide continued, but Brian Gibson said he was friendly with one of the airmen in the cookhouse, who told him they definitely added an unknown powder to the tea urns.

Everyone looked forward to Wednesdays – it was pay day and also sports afternoon. Bob found the procedure for collecting your princely sum of £2.00 (£1.7s.6d if you were National Service) very antiquated and, with a surname that began with "W", very boring.

I think I will change my name to Adams...

Everyone paraded in front of a table at which were seated the Paying Officer, flanked by two clerks. One or two SPs were present, presumably in case an airman decided it would be nice to help himself to all those pound notes the officer had piled in front of him. When the distributing of the enormous payouts started, one of the clerks would call out "AC2 Arrowsmith, G." The airman concerned would then shout "Sir!", come smartly to attention and march to the table. He would shout out the last three numbers of his service number, salute with his right hand and hold out his left hand.

This was a procedure that everyone seemed to get right, even Taffy Jones. The other clerk would read out his due amount and the officer would count out the coins and notes and place them in Arrowsmith's left hand. Arrowsmith would then salute again, turn smartly to the left and march off to count his new wealth. The sad thing was, there would usually be a colleague or two waiting with their hands out, ready to collect the loans they were owed. The boring bit for Bob was that pay parades were always conducted in alphabetical order, so with a parade of around 100 airmen, he was always one of the last to be paid and by the time he got to the NAAFI, all the cream buns had gone!

Wednesday was also sports afternoon when a variety of sports were on offer. The choice was usually cross-country running, cross-country running or, if you were lucky, cross-country running. This usually entailed donning your RAF issue plimsoles, RAF vests PT and RAF shorts PT (to keep your knees warm) and then spend the afternoon following a PT Instructor on his pushbike.

All very technical and carefully designed to hone you to the peak of physical fitness.

Just follow me lads ... it is only five miles!

Wednesday evening was usually a free evening, with only your own kit to get ready for the next day. Bob and Brian Gibson decided they would watch television on the only set available to all the airmen on camp. This was in the TV room at the NAAFI and had an enormous 17-inch screen and only two channels; BBC and ITV. This restriction of choice made life a lot easier when deciding which programme to watch, it simply meant that 25 people wanted to watch BBC and 25 people wanted to watch ITV. Typical ingredients for a fight, which were frequent. On this occasion they had to sit through the delights of *Coronation Street*, with Ena Sharples, et al. But at least it was free and a punch-up was included. The classics and live entertainment all in one evening – a lot of people paid good money for less...

Their training went on apace and they started to learn more about firearms, not just how to clean them. They were now familiar with the Bren gun and could dismantle and reassemble one in just a few minutes. They even knew the correct procedure when a gun stopped firing and clearing a gas jam. The one thing Bob never had the opportunity to do throughout his service was to fire a real Bren gun. He guessed that was because the Bren had a rapid rate of fire, which used up a lot of ammunition, and bullets were expensive. It was cheaper to wave a 20-year-old Lee Enfield .303 at the enemy.

They did, however, manage to fire .22 rifles on the Wednesford range and towards the end of their time at Wednesford they were taken to a full size range locally and were allowed to fire .303 rifles (not their worn-out drill rifles, with wooden stocks that were loosened to make rifle drills sound more impressive). When their day on the short .22 range finally came, Brian Gibson said the session would probably be taken by a *Rock Ape*. Bob did not like to show his ignorance to enquire further, but he could not really imagine the RAF had tame primates bright enough to fire a rifle – but then he thought of the average Drill Instructor and decided nothing was impossible.

Eventually they found themselves on the range with six mats laid out under a corrugated iron roof. Facing this building and about 25 yards away was a long brick wall, about ten feet high, with sandbags piled in front of it. In front of the sandbags were six cardboard targets, nine inches square. So the scene was set and everyone was a bit excited, although they would not admit it – all except Terry Nash, that is. Terry was a bit of a conscientious objector and had bored the other occupants of the hut to tears on many an evening with his lectures on the benefits of the strange views he held about most things. Terry's view was that guns were killing machines and why did we need to practice killing people?

We all went into Lichfield on a 12-hour pass the following Saturday, all except Terry, and when we returned Terry was not to be seen and all his belongings had gone from his lockers. We did not see him again.

We were told to *stand easy* by Corporal Jones while we waited for the firearms instructor. Eventually, the instructor arrived; he looked as though he could go 15 rounds with Bruce Woodcock. There was no sign of hair below his beret and his creases were razor-sharp. Bob decided he must be the best-dressed ape he had seen, but it was the corporal's shoulder flashes that explained the nickname *Rock-Ape*. The shoulder flashes said "RAF REGIMENT" and Brian explained that they had earned the nickname from their time on Gibraltar (where there is a famous colony of feral apes). Everyone referred to them as Rock-Apes, but never to their faces. They were the nearest thing the RAF had to the Paras.

Despite his intimidating looks, the corporal was very helpful and turned out to have incredible patience – and with Taffy Jones in the group, he certainly needed it. He demonstrated that we had to lay face down, with our legs slightly apart to stabilise the body. Both elbows were on the ground with the left hand supporting the rifle by the wooden part halfway along its length, the right hand held the gun around the trigger area and pulled the butt into the right shoulder, this hand was used to pull the trigger and also to operate the bolt that fed bullets into the gun. Quite simple really and even Taffy got this bit right when they had a dummy run.

However, Bob discovered that he, in fact, was going to be the problem child on this one…

Although he was right-handed, Bob could not close his left eye and keep his right eye open in order to look through the rifle sights, it also felt strange to him that he had to support the heavy rifle with his weakest arm. At this stage the corporal's patience was obviously wearing thin and he told Bob to fire in the way he felt most comfortable, as long as the gun pointed in the right general direction! Obviously he had little faith in the outcome and they all proceeded to fire five rounds at their respective targets. Bob struggled to operate the bolt because his left hand was the trigger hand but the bolt was on the right of the rifle, but with a bit of shuffling and a lot of grunting he got there.

They all managed to get their rounds into the target, even Taffy, although three of his rounds went into the target on his left and the other two into the target on his right! To everyone's surprise, especially Bob's, he was one of only three that managed to get all their rounds into a group of one inch diameter. On a 25-yard .22 range this was good enough to be classed as a marksman. 'Not bad for a cack-handed shot,' he thought. Now they had all fired real bullets from a real gun they were beginning to feel like real defenders of the Crown but, of course, as they were find out later, one swallow does not make a summer.

A new corporal was becoming more and more involved with them as time went on and rumour had it that Corporal Jones was due for demob, which probably explained why he had been quite civilised since their weekend leave. The new corporal was Corporal Atkins and, as they chatted one night in their billet, everyone seemed to think he seemed OK, although Dusty Miller was not too sure, as he had heard Corporal Atkins talking to a sergeant and the words, "I will soon sort them out" had been part of the conversation.

A couple of days later, Corporals Jones and Atkins both appeared on one of their morning parades and Corporal Jones confirmed he was indeed being demobbed and that Corporal Atkins would be taking over their Flight. He was from Colchester and Corporal Jones said he was sure Corporal Atkins would make sure their Flight was the best at Wednesford by the time they passed out.

The next morning Corporal Atkins took over completely and said that at 15.00hrs he was going to hold a hut and kit inspection and they were all to be standing beside their beds, dressed in their Best Blue. He then dismissed them and told them to get ready for the inspection. Someone said that Colchester was the Services Detention Centre. Had Corporal Atkins been an inmate or a guard? This created a debate, although Dusty said that maybe he just *lived* in Colchester. Views were about to be polarised into "was he in or out."

At 3 o'clock sharp Corporal Atkins appeared in the doorway and instructed them to stand to attention beside their beds. Then began the worst inspection they had experienced in their long six weeks as airmen. Complete kit layouts were thrown on the floor, bedpacks were pulled to pieces and coke thrown on their highly polished floor. At one stage he stood behind Tommy Davis and shouted, "Am I hurting you lad?"

"No Corporal," said Tommy.

"Well I should be. I am standing on your bloody hair!" was the reply. "Get it cut and report to me at 8 o'clock tonight!"

The inspection was finally over and Corporal Atkins said that if that was the standard they were used to then things were going to change and there would be a kit inspection every day until they got it right, starting in 3 hours time. An instant air of gloom descended on everyone and Tommy

Davis said, "Do you realise we have got this horrible little man looking after us for the next two or three weeks? What can we do about it lads?" All manner of quite nasty schemes were plotted, from a group of lads arranging to meet him somewhere dark and quiet to sabotaging his motor bike. It was soon realised however that it would be obvious who the culprits were and the punishment could be worse than the current situation, the heated planning meeting then gradually petered out as they all returned to their own bed-space to prepare for the next kit inspection.

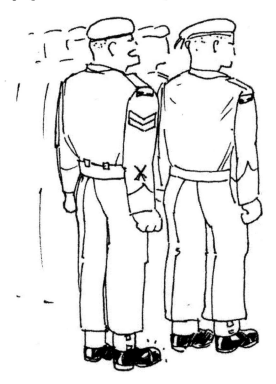

"Am I hurting you lad? I should be.
I am standing on your ruddy hair!"

The kit inspection went ahead and was only marginally less painful than the last one. At one stage Corporal Atkins was sounding off about the state of John Berry's boots and was standing all of twelve inches away from John's face.

"Have you been gardening in your boots airman?" and "Look at me when I talk to you!" were shouted loud enough for anyone on the parade ground 200 yards away to hear. John had spent hours on his boots with the handle of a spoon, loads of Cherry Blossom and a fair amount of spit, but for some reason the toecaps still looked below par. Even Harry Sharp had tried to get some life into them, but had given up. John Berry had the sense to hold his tongue, but it was obvious he was seething inside.

Eventually Corporal Atkins moved on to Bob's bed and started pulling his kit about and he then walked round to face Bob. Bob naturally kept looking at the Corporal; he did not want the same treatment as Harry.

"Why are you looking at me like that?" shouted the horrible little man. "Do you fancy me lad?"

"No Corporal," Bob said, and hoped he would go away, which fortunately he did.

The kit inspection came to an end at around 4.30pm, just time for a leisurely smoke before their evening meal… No chance! The horrible little man had them on the parade ground for half-an-hour's drill practice: "To give you an appetite." It certainly did that all right – but it was not just the food they were looking forward to attacking.

The next day, after their kit inspection, which came with its now-to-be-expected shouting, ranting and raving, they were marched to the classrooms for a subject simply called *Passive Defence*. They watched a film showing a nuclear explosion and the devastating effects it had on properties and people over a very wide area. Even more worrying was the length of time it took for the effects of a nuclear explosion to disappear and they learnt the meaning of such phrases as *half-life*. This, they were told, was the number of years it took radioactivity to reduce by half in certain objects and substances, like soil and bricks.

The frightening thing was they learnt that in some cases it took longer in some cases than years left in their life. They were then taught how to protect themselves in the case of a nuclear blast and what their priorities should be if they survived.

"Blimey" said Frank Simmons. "This makes the 1914 trenches look like a picnic!"

In fact, sitting round the stove that night, they all generally agreed there was not a lot of point in continuing with their training because they were not going to survive long enough to put it into practice. Learning to fire a .303 rifle was a little bit like peeing into the wind, they decided.

But then they remembered tomorrow's kit inspection and things were normal again...

The next morning was taken up firstly with the kit inspection, which was now becoming normal to them. Even the corporal's rantings and ravings were now known off by heart and were fast becoming material for the frustrated impersonators among them to use in their wisecracks.

If the kit inspection was a bit non-eventful, Corporal Atkins must have had an argument with someone during the Naafi break, because on the square after the break he was obviously looking for trouble and they could do nothing right. Taffy got himself into a right muddle when sloping and presenting arms. The horrible little man called Taffy just about every derogatory name Bob had ever heard and a few he hadn't.

Eventually, after making Taffy practice the slope and present six times on his own in front of everyone, he made him march at the double round the parade ground three times while they all watched. This was probably the lowest point in the morale of the Flight in the whole of their stay at Wednesford, and something they would probably never forget or forgive.

Fortunately they did not see Corporal Atkins any more that day because they were back in the Education Section in the afternoon to learn more about self-defence. This time they were shown how to use various parts of their equipment and specifically what effects a gas attack could have. Things like Nerve Gas and Mustard Gas had pretty gruesome effects on the human body, they learnt, and this was graphically demonstrated in a very explicit film. They rehearsed the procedure they should adopt in the event of a gas attack, although the gas mask and cape they would be issued with seemed a poor defence. They were then taken outside to a disused air raid shelter for what their instructor promised them would be 'the highlight of the afternoon'.

They were issued with a gas mask each and told to practice fitting it properly, checking each other's masks for correct fitting. The instructor then asked if they were very sure their masks were fitted correctly. A group "Yes Corporal!" was the shout, albeit muffled by the gas masks.

"Right then... get in single file and go in through the green door. When you get inside, I want you to form a large circle with both hands on the shoulders of the man in front of you."

Once they had sorted themselves out, the corporal said he would be leaving, whereupon gas would be pumped into the room and they would be given further instructions by loudspeaker. Once again the word 'Holocaust' came into Bob's head, although this soon disappeared once the door closed on the corporal and they received simple drill movements over the loudspeaker.

"Left turn... right turn... about turn..." the loudspeaker instructed.

'Well,' thought Bob, 'at least I have fitted my mask properly, but perhaps they are kidding us and there is no gas in here after all.'

With that, the loudspeaker told them to return to the circle and place their hands on the shoulders of the man in front. They should then start to walk round in a circle at the same time singing a verse of the "Happy Wanderer", but before that they must all remove their masks.

"Remove your masks and start walking and singing," the loudspeaker instructed. With that, the lights dimmed to a glow and they all felt complete idiots walking in a circle with arms round a mate and singing silly songs – if only Mum could see me now. After what seemed a lifetime, the lights came on, the door opened and they were instructed to file out into the fresh air.

Once outside they were met by the scene of a group of fully grown men standing in a group, crying their eyes out and coughing and spluttering. 'A bit like a group of Capstan-smoking football supporters after their team has just lost the cup final,' thought Bob.

It was explained to them that the gas they had experienced was simply a very low dose of tear gas and it would have no lasting effects. If that was a low dose, heaven help anyone who was subjected to the real thing!

That evening was very subdued in their hut, as most of them were still suffering the ill-effects of the gas, but what made them even more serious was the treatment Corporal Atkins had handed out to Taffy. The general feeling was that the horrible little man's behaviour should be reported, but Dusty Miller said his older brother had been subject to similar behaviour in the Army last year and that complaining had only made matters worse. Taking the complaint path was therefore decided against, but to a man they vowed to get their own back somehow. Talking to a Flight that was due to pass out at the end of the week, Bob learnt that in their last week they had taken part in a night exercise. An idea began to form in Bob's mind and he decided to get more information from the outgoing Flight.

The next day was a day away from Corporal Atkins because they all piled onto a truck and were taken to a local Army rifle range. This was the real thing, with big targets 200 yards from their firing position and this time they would be using full size .303 rifles. These were still fairly old Lee Enfields, similar to their drill rifles, but in much better condition. The sergeant in charge of the range explained the procedure, which was fairly identical to that on the 25 yard range, although the rifles were bigger and the targets much further away.

There was one big difference however... The sergeant asked for six volunteers for *butt duty*, but as no-one seemed to know what this was, there were no volunteers. (They had only been in the RAF for a few weeks but they had already learnt one important lesson – never volunteer for anything!) Having no volunteers, the sergeant detailed six men for the mysterious "Butt Duty" and instructed them to follow him down the range to the targets.

From the firing position the targets had appeared to be on two poles and were about two feet off the ground, but as they approached the targets it was obvious that the bottom of the poles were in a trench about four feet deep with an earth bank behind it. The sergeant explained that their job was to be in the trench and change the targets when they were instructed to do so.

At this point, two things were obvious:
1.) They were all more than four feet tall and
2.) They now knew why he had asked for volunteers!

The sergeant explained further that the corporal in charge of the butts was in contact with him by field telephone and would only instruct them to change targets when he was told it was safe to do so and all rifles had been checked and were empty. Between target changes the lads were to sit in the trench with their backs to the rifles. "All very safe," they were assured. Ha! Ha!

"Even the birds are waving a white flag."

With that, the day's shooting was about to start, the corporal shouted "everyone down" and they all had to sit on the earth beneath their respective targets.

Suddenly, all hell let loose, with the crack of the rifles, the whistle of bullets over their head and spurts of earth erupting in the bank in front of them. Everyone was nervously looking for the nearest toilet.

Suddenly everything went quiet and the corporal shouted "change targets!" They all stood up and replaced the targets, repeating this procedure three times until it was their turn at the other end of the range.

"Now I know what they mean by *up to your eyes in muck and bullets*," said Dusty, and wondered how they could persuade Corporal Atkins to join them in the Butts. In the meantime Bob's plan was progressing in his mind, but he decided to keep it to himself for the time being.

Bob did not manage to repeat his grouping when he took his turn with the .303, mainly because he found the bolt very difficult to operate with the wrong hand and because his mind was on other things. The Flight did quite well, however, and the Range Sergeant congratulated them on their overall performance, suggesting that the better ones among them might want to consider joining the RAF Regiment when they completed their basic training. 'Not likely,' thought Bob.

The next morning Corporal Atkins was back with a vengeance. Harry Sharp had spent all night in the toilet and had attended sick parade. He was therefore late joining Corporal Atkins morning drill practice.

"Thank you for turning up," was the sarcastic greeting he received from Corporal Atkins. "It is nice of you to join us."

We continued with our drill although, due to the delicate state of his stomach, Harry Sharp found marching a trifle difficult. As a result, he once again became the recipient of Corporal Atkins venom, with the shouted comment, "Open those legs Sharp, nothing will fall out!" ringing across the parade ground.

Harry Sharp's illness was not the only pain in the backside on the parade ground that day and Bob decided that he would put his plan to the rest of the hut that night.

"Excuse me Sir ... but shouldn't they
unfix bayonets before they port arms?"

They were now nearing the end of their time at Wednesford and were spending more and more time rehearsing for their passing-out parade. It was still winter and quite often when they went to breakfast there was a light covering of frost on the ground. On Friday afternoon Corporal Atkins announced their Flight would have a full rehearsal the following morning; he obviously wanted to watch Wolves play in the afternoon, so he said they would parade at 8.00am sharp. The practice parade ground was on a slight slope and during the night it has rained. The next morning there had been a frost, which was still very evident when they formed up for the parade, complete with greatcoats, webbing belts, boots and rifles. They were soon to find out that wet, sloping tarmac, a frost and metal-studded boots are a dangerous combination. No sooner had Corporal Atkins shouted, "Flight, in threes, by the right quick ... march!" than something resembling opening day at the Harrod's sale crossed with a full-blown rugby scrum developed, with legs, arms and rifles going in all directions. Language befitting the moment was interspersed with the groans of the injured. When everyone managed to sort themselves out, there were an assortment of injuries, a broken leg, two broken fingers and numerous cuts and bruises. Someone called the medics, who were soon on the scene, but there was no sign of Corporal Atkins!

When they eventually got back to their billet, Bob decided to talk to the lads about his plan and they sat around the fire and had a council of war. Harry Sharp was a bit dubious and thought that although Corporal Atkins was a nasty character, he was only doing his job and, after all, they only had to put up with him for a couple more weeks. Taffy, however, normally a quiet and peaceful chap, was really wound up with hate for the "horrible creature" that had made his life hell. The three stitches in the back of Taffy's head were still throbbing and did nothing to improve his view of the corporal. After much discussion they agreed a plan and all looked forward to an opportunity to put it into action.

The Passing Out parade for their entry was to be in one week's time. After the parade they would be given their next postings and then go home for ten days' leave.

The next week would seem to take forever to pass. The weather had started to change and instead of clear days and frosts they were having mild but damp days and nights and it was therefore decided to re-start the night exercises that had not been held in the cold weather. The exercises were held in the local woods and involved the Entry being divided into Red and Blue troops with Red troop attacking and Blue troop defending a pole in the centre of a clearing in the woods. This pole represented a nuclear store and they were briefed that no holds were barred when it came to tactics, although physical injury was barred, as were any types of weapon. Their only weapons were sticks of blue or red chalk, with which they had to place a cross on the backs of the enemy they "captured" or "killed".

The afternoon of the exercise was spent with a corporal from the RAF Regiment, briefing them on tactics, things to avoid and how to conceal yourself. Bob's flight was to be Red troop and had to attack the target. They were issued with waterproof jackets, red armbands, camouflage nets, face blacking and a map of the woods. They were to appoint their own leader and plan their own tactics; their Drill Instructors would act as referees.

"Watch out for the RAF Regiment, they are sneaky so-and-sos..."

At 10 o'clock they were driven to the woods and left in two areas, one for the Reds and one nearer the target for the Blues. Bob had been appointed leader for the Reds and they had held a long briefing session, planning just what their tactics would be and they were all looking forward to the night. They soon found that a strange wood in the dark can be a very nasty place to be, a lot different to the charming, leafy place it is the sunshine. The odd bog, brambles and strange noises made it far from pleasant, but they split into three groups as planned and set off to follow their chosen routes to the clearing. There were four lads in Bob's group and apart from an argument with some barbed wire they had a fairly uneventful journey to the clearing. They were congratulating themselves on how well they had done when the trees around them sprang into life and two of their group were promptly "chalked" and led away. Bob and Brian Gibson managed to escape and re-grouped, they had noticed that Corporal Atkins was the referee for the Blue group that had ambushed them. Bob and Brian then re-thought their plans and disappeared into the darkness.

At about midnight a whistle was blown to mark the end of the exercise and a bright floodlight was switched on for them to gather under. The results of the exercise were announced and mugs of hot tea were distributed and were very welcome. It was announced that Blue troop had been very successful in their defence of the target and they were pronounced the winners. Following the announcement they were told to make their way back to the transport and they would not be required to parade until after lunch the next day.

While everyone was together Bob said in a loud voice to Brian, "I saw Corporal Atkins creeping off early, he reckoned he had a date".

They all arrived back at their hut, washed off their blacking and turned in for a much needed sleep. They went to breakfast as usual and on the way back someone from the next hut said to them, "Did you hear about your corporal?"

"What about him?" said Bob, trying to keep a straight face.

"It seems that they could not find him last night and they assumed he had skived off, but at 5 o'clock this morning he turned up and said he had spent all night tied to a tree in the woods. Evidently two lads with black faces had ambushed him and tied him up."

Bob looked at Brian and winked.

"Some you lose and some you win," he said, and allowed a smile of self-satisfaction to show on his face.

The day of their passing out arrived and the parade went extremely well. They congratulated themselves for getting everything swinging in the same direction and at the same time as everyone else, and there were no right turns when everyone else left turned. Bit of a miracle really!

The Airmens' Mess put on a half-decent meal and they even had ice cream for pudding – obviously someone wanted them to leave Wednesford with good memories.

The next day they all said their goodbyes and, fully-loaded with their full webbing packs and kitbags, clambered onto trucks for the journey to the station. They each had a travel warrant to their home and another from their home to their new posting. In Bob's case this was to RAF St Agnes, somewhere in Wales.

5.   Learning a Trade

Arriving home, the first thing Bob did was to take off his uniform and put on some comfortable, smooth, soft clothes. The second thing he made sure he did was to tell his parents that he did not want to be paraded round to their relations, like a prize pig, and *definitely* no family parties.

He then had to decide what he wanted to do for the next ten days; this unaccustomed freedom was completely new to him. He decided to go into town and look up some of his old mates in their old haunts, but no matter where he looked he could find nobody. Jean in the local greasy spoon said "most of them have joined up like you. Those that haven't are probably out with their girlfriends." Bob suddenly felt lonely and went home to watch Hughie Green introducing people that could suck their own toes or sing *God Save The Queen* with a mouthful of baked beans. The only entertaining part of the show was the running commentary his dad kept up, with comments like, "If she's a singer, I'm Bing Crosby" and "I have seen funnier people at a funeral" were shouted at the television. For once his dad and mum agreed on something, that the television programmes were rubbish, but they still sat there and watched them until the National Anthem was played and the little dot gradually disappeared into the centre of the screen.

The next day Bob decided to do some shopping and spend some of the fortune the RAF had paid him on new clothes. After all, he was an adult now and had an image to keep up. He looked in Burtons window and a nice pair of trousers caught his eye. He had only just caught up with the fashion and had started wearing the tight-legged trousers that the lads called *drainpipes*, although he had definitely decided not to wear the long, highly-coloured jackets the "Teddy Boys" wore. After all, there was no way his haircut could be classed as a D.A. and he would look daft as a Teddy Boy with his cropped short back and sides. Anyway, he was getting fed-up with having to take his shoes off every time he changed his trousers and trousers with bigger legs would get over that problem. So off he went and bought a pair of blue trousers with a feint red check on them and while he was in the shop he bought a dark blue knitted cardigan that he thought would go nicely with the trousers. The girl that served him told him he would look very smart.

He chatted to the girl while they waited for his receipt to come back on the wire device that took his money to the cash office and delivered his change and receipt back to him. He said that he was in the RAF and had just come home on leave. She seemed quite interested in this and told him she was only working in the shop while she waited to join the Police Force. Bob plucked up courage and asked her if she would like to meet him for a coffee in the newly opened Coffee Bar that evening and – surprise, surprise – she agreed.

Bob had a bath (showers were "for poofs" according to his dad) and donned his new trousers, his favourite shirt and new cardigan and walked down to the Coffee Bar where he had agreed to meet – oh dear, he didn't know her name. He sat there for about half an hour and was just about to leave, thinking he had been stood-up, when his date walked in the door. Bob hardly recognised her without her shop uniform and her hair looked much shorter than it had earlier. The girl said she was sorry to have kept him waiting and that she would explain why later.

When he said he did not know her name she said, " Of course, I haven't told you. It's Daphne."

Bob bought them both a coffee or two and they spent a long time just chatting about music and their families. Daphne mentioned that she had always wanted to join the Police and asked him what he did for a living. Bob thought it quite strange that a young girl had such a bad memory – after all, he told her only a few hours ago that he was on leave from the RAF. Daphne said it was time she was going home because she would have to be up early the next day as she was on the early shift at the factory. Now Bob was really confused, not only did she have a bad memory, she was also, for some reason, lying about her place of work. As they walked home they stopped and sat on a bench in the Garden of Remembrance and Bob plucked up the courage to steal a kiss, which to his surprise Daphne returned warmly, sending a funny feeling through his body.

'Obviously the bromide is wearing off,' he thought.

As they sat there, with Bob's arm around her, Daphne said, "I have a confession to make. I am not the girl you met in Burton's this afternoon."

'Blimey,' thought Bob. 'I have read about people like you. What next?'

"That was my twin sister Pam, but she had a migraine tonight and is in bed with the curtains drawn. Rather than let you down I said I would take her place."

"But you said you wanted to join the Police," said Bob.

"I do," said Daphne. "We both want to join as soon as we are old enough"

Now Bob was really confused. He had liked Pam enough to ask her for a date, but now he had been on a date with her sister, who had set things tingling inside him.

'To hell with it!' he thought. The girls have planned a bit of fun at my expense. Well two can play that game. I will date them both. Neither will tell the other and it could brighten the next ten days. So Bob had gone from no female distraction to having two girls he fancied – and one at least who fancied him. If they were both as warm and friendly as Daphne, then this could make for an enjoyable leave.

The next day Bob paid a visit to Burtons and made arrangements to meet Pam outside the Odeon that evening. They met as arranged and went for a drink at the Black & White Milk Bar before going to the cinema. As they drank their cups of milky tea, Pam said she was sorry she could not meet him the previous evening and how did he get on with her sister?

"Alright," said Bob. "But I think she felt a bit sorry for me and didn't really like me."

"Really?" said Pam. "I must admit she was a bit quiet when she came home, but then she is not really into boys."

'Interesting,' thought Bob. 'Let's hope her sister is…'

The film being shown at the Odeon was a war film and Pam asked him to tell her all about the aircraft, seeing as he was an airman. What an opportunity to impress the fairer sex!

"Oh," he said, knowledgeably, "they are Spitfires, with their fantastic Rolls Royce V12 engines. They were such good aircraft that America bought hundreds of them and they have even been shooting down the Mig jets in Korea. They often break the sound barrier and I expect I shall be repairing them when I go back. I might even get a chance to fly one."

Those 'Spitfires' were in fact P47 Thunderbolts and their Rolls Royce V12 engines were Pratt and Whitney radials. What did Bob know? But at least his date was impressed. They both enjoyed the film and Bob even managed to put his arm around Pam before she made the excuse that she had dropped something on the floor and moved away from him.

As they said goodnight Bob said, "It might be as well if you didn't tell Daphne you were going out with me. I think it might upset her." Pam agreed and, after arranging to meet Bob at the weekend, she gave him a quick peck on the cheek and ran for the bus.

'So far so good,' thought Bob. 'Now to see if Daphne will come out with me...'

The next evening he stood outside the factory when the hooter sounded and waited for Daphne to appear. Eventually she came out, along with two of her workmates, both about Bob's age, and they all stopped when Daphne stopped to talk to Bob.

'Well,' thought Bob. 'At least I have a choice of two others if Daphne turns me down,' but she told her friends to go on and she would catch them up. She seemed pleased to see Bob and readily agreed to meet him at the Odeon that night.

"Oh, by the way," said Bob. "It might be as well not to mention it to your sister. I think it would upset her."

That evening, as they watched the war film, Bob explained it all to her.

"How do you know so much about it?" asked Daphne.

"Oh, it comes as second nature to us Air Force types," said Bob, nonchalantly.

With Daphne he was able to keep his arm around her for most of the film and even got a couple of decent kisses.

'You're in here, lad,' he thought, and went home that night feeling quite pleased with himself.

The rest of the leave was spent trying to organise dates with the two sisters so that neither of the girls saw him with the other. By the skin of his teeth, he managed it, while having some very enjoyable times with both girls. If he had learnt anything on this leave, it was how to behave with the opposite sex, how to be devious and that one of the sisters was not a true blonde! He intended to find out about the other one on his next leave and decided he would write to both of them while he was away. The problem was, how could he do that without the two girls comparing postmarks and handwriting on the envelope?

He thought up an ingenious, foolproof plan. He would write normally to Daphne and would also write to Pam but get a mate at camp to address the envelope for him. He would then send this letter in the sealed envelope to his young brother and ask him to post it in their home town. It would cost him a few records when he was next on leave, but Bob reckoned the end result would be worth it and he looked forward to his next leave when he looked forward to solving the mystery of the blonde.

The ten days leave were soon up and Bob found himself on the train from Paddington to Wales. There were about six others on the train that were obviously going to RAF St Agnes, and one of them was Chris Milne, a lad he knew from Wednesford. A truck met them and, after a forty-five minute journey, they arrived at St Agnes. Two things struck Bob immediately, the absence of squads of marching airmen accompanied by loud, slightly hoarse DIs and the presence of a real live airfield with the whistling noise of jet engines.

They found that life at St Agnes was going to be a lot easier than it had been at Wednesford, with just one parade per week and the occasional kit inspection. Bull nights and hut inspections were still a weekly feature and the huts were very similar to Wednesford, with their coke stoves, polished lino floors and pads to walk on. One item was missing from the huts however, the rifle rack which at Wednesford had held all their rifles. RAF St Agnes was divided into two separate sites, one holding the training school of which Bob was part, and the other accommodating the permanent staff, who Bob was told were responsible for carrying out the big maintenance jobs on aircraft.

There were about 30 new arrivals and they were addressed by the Wing Commander in charge of the School of Technical Training, who told them they would be known as "202 Entry". Some of them would become "Pistons" and some "GT's", which he explained were gas turbines. They would all be stationed there for twelve weeks, after which, as long as they passed their examinations, they would become Ac1 (Aircraftsmen 1st Class) Engine Mechanics GT or Piston. They were then divided into their respective classes and told to report to their classrooms the following morning. Bob found out he was to be a "GT" and was very surprised to find a couple of females on his section, his first taste of meeting the female section of the RAF, known as "Waafs" but really WRAF (Women's Royal Air Force). Not surprisingly, the two Waafs were not in his hut, but had their own accommodation elsewhere on the camp.

The next morning all the GT's made their way to classroom E15 and waited in line in the corridor. Shortly afterwards a man in his 50s, in a brown dustcoat, arrived and led them into the classroom.

"Good morning," he said. "My name is Mr Davis and I will be your instructor for most of your stay here." He sorted them out into rows of six, just like being at school again. As they sat behind their desks he outlined the principle of the gas turbine engine and gave them some idea of what their course would consist of. He then took them down to the stores to collect their denims and their notebooks. While outlining the principles of the gas turbine engine, Mr Davis said "If I ever hear any of you mention the word *blowlamp*, I will personally put you on a charge."

The afternoon was spent learning the different types of thread you could find on a bolt, depending on whether it was BA, Whitworth or British Standard Pipe, where you would find these bolts and the different types of nuts and washers that went with them. All a bit boring, thought Bob, and he could not see what this had to do with aircraft. He was surprised, however, to find the two girls were usually the first to put their hands up in answer to questions and they usually had the right answer. On top of all this boring detail about threads, they had to revise during the evening in preparation for the regular morning examination.

They had all started to get to know each other by the evening and Bob had become quite proficient at sussing out who the bright ones were and who would help him out if had a problem question – in other words, who he should sit next to in the classroom.

The first three or four weeks of training really was basic engineering practice, learning how to use a hacksaw or a file and finding out what *Dzus Fasteners* and *Oddie Fasteners* were. *Intercrystaline corrosion* was no longer something from outer space and he could even tell the composition of a sheet of metal simply by using caustic soda and noting the colour it turned the metal.

Bob had met up with Ted White, who was also part of 202 Entry. Ted lived in London and owned an Austin 12. He said he wanted to start a car-sharing pool for return journeys to London at weekends and, ever mindful of the twin delights awaiting him at home, Bob joined the car pool and wrote to his ladies-in-waiting to let them know he would be coming home at the weekend. Bob thought it a bit odd, however, that he had not heard from either of them for a couple of weeks, although he was not too concerned, because he knew they were about to enter the Police Training College.

Friday eventually came and as soon as their instructor dismissed them on Friday afternoon, they all piled into the Austin and set off for Cardiff and the A40. Four bum-numbing hours later they arrived in central London and Ted dropped them all off in the Strand, outside Charing Cross station, arranging to meet them in the same place at 9.00pm on Sunday evening.

Bob just managed to get the last train home, followed by a two-mile walk from the station. Bob's parents thought he was mad doing that journey just for one and a half days at home, but Bob had his sights set on solving the mystery of the hair colour and successfully resolving that question would definitely make the journey worthwhile.

It was not to be, however, because the girls had actually started their police training course and were currently living at the police college.

Bob visited all his old haunts and managed to date one of his girlfriends from his last year at school, but it became obvious that she was not really interested in a long-distance relationship. In fact, she was not interested in any sort of relationship and Bob suddenly remembered her nickname from school – *Tin Drawers*!

After a very boring weekend, Bob made his way back to Charing Cross Station and the Strand. After a worrying wait, Ted White eventually turned up, 45 minutes late. It seems Ted had been more successful with his female relationships over the weekend and it became more and more obvious that he had not had his full quota of sleep. Following one or two hairy escapades on the twisting, turning A40, they finished up with their front wheels hanging over the river on a sharp bend just outside Newport. At this stage, Ted suddenly became more awake and they finished the journey without further incident.

Their training was becoming more interesting now and they actually got to see a real jet engine. This was a specially cut-away Rolls Royce Derwent exhibited on a metal stand in the training school. The first things Bob noticed were the colour-coded pipes and cables – so much for his so-called 'colour perception problem'! They were told the Derwent was very similar in basic design to the original gas turbine engine invented by Frank Whittle. This was where their instructor warned them yet again about not calling it a 'blowlamp', although he admitted the noise produced by both was very similar. But that was where the similarity ended. He explained that air entered the front of the engine, was mixed with fuel in the combustion chamber and ignited. The hot air expanded and was then forced out from the chamber through a smaller hole. As he explained, if you reduce the volume of the air you increase its speed and this is the basic principle of the gas turbine engine.

There was, of course, far more than this to a gas turbine. For example, how do you get air into the engine when it is standing still? They were to learn the answer to this question and many more, including some they had not even thought of, during their remaining weeks at St Agnes.

They learnt that the BPC was the *Barometric Pressure Control*, a device that controlled the fuel entering the engine as the aircraft gained height and entered lower air pressure, the atmospheric pressure obviously affecting the amount of fuel required by the engine. They realised that the engine gearbox was not there so that the pilot could perform racing gear changes; its purpose was to take power from the engine to drive the various air, oil and hydraulic pumps required in a modern aircraft.

They were all totally engrossed in their training and spent most evenings revising that day's work, ready for the following morning's question time. They had now actually graduated to a real Meteor aircraft for part of their lessons and the first warning they received before even looking in the cockpit was: "Beware of Ejection Seats!"

This Meteor was an early model and not fitted with an Ejector Seat, but they were shown a real seat by their instructor, who pointed out the very dangerous cable that ran from the handle above the pilot's head to the top of the tube that contained the explosive used to force the seat out of the aircraft and propel it around twenty or thirty feet clear of the crashing aircraft. He explained that if you leant on this wire it would activate the firing mechanism and you would find yourself draped across a heavy ejector seat being propelled about thirty feet into the air at very high speed. As most hangar roofs were only eighteen feet high, this had a tendency to make a nasty mess on the inside of the roof, which was not a very nice thing to clean up. Many stories went around of airmen who had made that short but fatal journey.

The simple way of preventing such an unwanted journey was to ensure that the safety pin, with its round red tag, was removed from its stowage in the side of the seat and placed in the make-safe position in the firing pin on top of the tube.

Don't touch the red lev…!

While they were being instructed, they all wore their rather shapeless denims, with press-studs at the ankles and wrists. As they were familiarising themselves with the cockpit fuel and throttle controls one day, Bob decided that he would "goose" Ted, who was leaning over with his head in the cockpit and his feet on the ladder. As he performed his "how's that then" movement there was an extremely loud scream and a very red-faced Waaf emerged from the cockpit, much to Bob's embarrassment. To make matters worse, it was not even the good looking one! Fortunately, the instructor was nowhere to be seen and after a lot of humble apologies and promises of cream buns in the Naafi, the matter was not pursued. Bob felt privately that she was quite excited by it really, especially as he had noticed her giving him a sly smile or two recently, but Bob's thoughts were focussed on the twins at home, so he decided to save himself.

He had not heard from either of the twins, but a friend of his at home had told his Mum that they were still on their police training course. It was his Mum's birthday, so Bob decided to endure the mind- and bum-numbing car journey home for the weekend on the chance he might see them.

The journey to London was uneventful until just past Oxford, when three Police cars, with their bells ringing, suddenly blocked them in and eight very large coppers surrounded their car. They thought at first that it was some sort of joke, but it soon became apparent that the Police were deadly serious, because they were ordered out of the car and told to sit on the pavement with their hands on their heads.

The Police then proceeded to take everything out of the car and empty their holdalls. After what seemed like a lifetime, one of the coppers shouted, "Its all right lads, they have got them cornered in Oxford!" With that, the sergeant said, "Sorry, we must go, a car like yours with four lads in it was seen leaving a robbery and we thought it was you."

They jumped in their cars and roared off, leaving the lads belongings in a heap by the roadside. As they left, one copper was heard to say to another, "I knew it wasn't them, they were too scruffy." It did nothing to improve their view of the Oxfordshire police.

They eventually arrived in London, but by this time Bob had missed his last train, so he had to spend the night at Charing Cross and catch the milk train down early in the morning. As the local bus drivers were still in bed at that early hour, he had to walk the three miles home, arriving just as the first bus from town passed him!

He hoped that after such a rotten journey he might have a bit more luck with the twins, but not so, he was told they were on a team-building weekend in the Welsh mountains and would not be back for three days.

Bob looked around for some female company for the evening, but all the single girls now had boyfriends – his mates. Even "Tin Drawers" had a friend, a very masculine looking girl with short straight hair and what Bob definitely thought was a moustache. There was nothing for it, even his Dad would not go for a drink and leave his Mum on her birthday, so Bob took his Mum and Dad out for a meal (which his Dad paid for) and they all tucked into a Chef and Brewer steak and chips meal with a bottle of Blue Nun to celebrate.

The weekend over, Bob made his way back to London to start the nightmare journey back to camp. On the way up Ted had promised he would get some sleep this time and they all agreed that they would stop more often, as long as it was not in Oxfordshire, and also sing "Eskimo Nell" to keep the driver awake. Their tactics obviously worked because they arrived back at camp all in one piece and with their trousers the same colour as when they started.

There were now two weeks to the end of their course and the main topic of conversation was where they would be posted to next; somewhere in the British Isles or abroad perhaps? They had all been asked for their preference, but the permanent station staff at St Agnes had told them it did not make a lot of difference what you asked for. As Bob at that time had his mind well and truly fixed on his twins, he had requested a UK posting, but now he did not really mind where he went.

They were now in the final stages of becoming fully-trained aircraft engine mechanics and the final few days were to be spent on aircraft handling, including engine runs. This was when you sat in the cockpit and pretended you were a pilot, the idea being that you went through the rather complicated starting procedure and actually, if you were lucky, managed to start both engines on the training Meteor. If you were unlucky and got the sequence wrong, you could have what was known as a "Wet Start", when a few gallons of unburnt fuel collected in the engine and it would not start.

The solution to this situation was to shut everything down and for two or three lads to jump on the tail, forcing it to the ground so that the unburnt fuel drained off onto the tarmac. This procedure took time and cost money, so if you had a wet start it definitely lost you brownie points with the Instructor.

The day came for Bob's group to do their engine runs and they made their way out to a remote corner of the airfield, where a tired-looking retired Meteor was parked. It may have looked worn-out and scruffy, but to Bob it was the aircraft of his dreams, in which he would zoom off to numerous "dogfights". But before he could zoom anywhere he had to be able to start the damn thing…

It was a glorious, warm June day and they had to take their turn at manning the fire extinguishers and then getting into the cockpit for the ultimate experience. Now, as we know, Bob had a surname that began with "W", which automatically put him at the end of any RAF queue, so after watching a couple of "A's" do their starts, Bob and Ginger Thompson lay down on the grass to enjoy the sun. Bob then fell asleep and was eventually shaken awake by the Instructor. It seems he and Ginger had been asleep for over an hour and this was immediately obvious to Bob because his face felt quite sore from the hot sun. Ginger was in a bit of a state however, being ginger he had reacted very badly to the sun and had developed some nasty-looking blisters on his face. He was taken off to Sick Quarters for treatment and then put on a charge for "being unavailable for duty due to self-inflicted injuries".

Once Ginger had been despatched and normality resumed, it was Bob's turn for his engine run and he climbed into the cockpit. 'Now take a deep breath,' he said to himself 'and remember the correct start sequence. His brain was now working overtime: 'Should the LP cock be "on" or "off"? What about the HP cock? Where should the throttle lever be set? Don't forget to switch the tank pumps to "on". At what stage do I increase the throttle setting? Etc, etc…'

Then, like a miracle, the engine gradually increased its whine and the sound turned to a roar as ignition took place. Bob was reminded by the Instructor to set the throttle to "ground idle" and he repeated the procedure on the second engine. After a couple of minutes running, to check that various gauges were reading correctly and, most importantly, that the jet pipe temperatures were within the permitted range, the Instructor told him to shut the engines down. Bob climbed out of the cockpit and at that moment felt ten feet tall. In twenty minutes he had evolved from a struggling trainee into a full-blown Engine Mechanic (GT) and boy was he proud!

That weekend was to be their last at St Agnes and a group of them decided to go to the local seaside resort on Saturday to celebrate. They split up and Bob and Ted set their sights on a couple of girls they met on the Big Dipper. The two girls both worked at the Steel Company of Wales and were spending the day together because their boyfriends had just joined the RAF and were doing their square-bashing, Bob did not ask which camp they were at, just in case it was Wednesford. They had an enjoyable afternoon and in the evening Bob and his new friend walked along the beach until they found a patch of grass under some trees. They sat down and swapped stories of their lives so far, the girl coming across as very intelligent and game for a laugh. They both respected their absent friends and restrained their obvious animal urges, although Bob did manage to add to his knowledge of all things female.

When he met Ted later it was obvious that Ted and his girl had not practised such restraint, as Ted's first call when he got back to camp was to the ET Room!

On the following Monday their final course marks and exam results were posted on the noticeboard, together with their postings. All of Bob's entry had managed to gain a pass and they were all now officially AC1 Engine Mechanics. The postings were to all points of the UK and to places like Germany, Aden and Kenya, but Bob was the only one listed to go to No.99 Maintenance Unit at RAF Brister, which evidently was somewhere in Oxfordshire, prompting bad thoughts of the local Constabulary. He had hoped he would be posted to a Squadron, but never mind, at least he would not have to put up with camels, sand or sauerkraut.

Once again Bob found himself on the back of a three-ton truck on his way to the station to catch the train to London and 10 days leave before joining his new unit. He had already used his devious communication methods to write to the twins and make dates with both of them on two different evenings. His mum was obviously glad to see him and had made him his favourite meal of liver and bacon.

"A girl called Daphne called round and said she would meet you as arranged tomorrow night," she said. "You didn't tell us about her. Are you serious about her Bob? Why not bring her home for a meal?"

Bob's immediate thoughts were:

a) yes and no

b) definitely no.

"Maybe I will one day," he replied.

The next day Bob spent the day shopping for a smart new shirt and he also paid a visit to his barber, although he was definitely not in need of a haircut. He arrived at the arranged meeting place in good time, freshly bathed and shaved and with a nice aftershave that his aunt had bought him for Christmas. Eventually Daphne walked round the corner and after the usual pleasantries said, "I hope you don't mind, Bob, but I have brought someone with me..." and with that, her sister Pam came round the corner, followed by two six-foot-plus blokes with size ten feet.

"I believe you know Pam," said Daphne. "And these are our boyfriends, both from the Police Force. Why don't you join us for the evening?"

It was obvious that the twins had each known about her sister's secret liaisons with Bob for some time and had set him up. Bob made his excuses, went home and made a bee-line for his bedroom, where he sulked all night. His mum and dad did not say a word. Maybe they were in on the joke too.

Needless to say, he never did find the answer to that blonde hair question.

Bob spent the rest of his leave trying to find a young lady on whom to lavish his charm and sophistication. Despite his many corny chat-up lines he was not very successful, although he did manage a bit of exploring in the back row of the cinema on one occasion. That was not a total success though, because she was not the brightest penny in the piggy-bank and he had to spend half the film explaining what was happening on screen. His hand would just be reaching an interesting point in the geography of her body when she would say, "Bob, what is he doing that for?" or "Bob, why is she crying?" – interrupting his carefully planned route.

Bob did not make any further plans to meet her again.

He found himself at a bit of a loose end really, all his old mates were at work and he missed the routines he had got used to over the past few months. He even agreed to help his dad out in the butcher's shop for a few days; at least he got to meet some female company there, although most of them had a couple of snotty-nosed kids in tow.

He spent the last day or so getting his uniform and kit ready for the next stage of his RAF career, something he was looking forward to now that he was a fully-qualified airman. He was uncertain how he should dress for his arrival at RAF Brister, so he decided he should play it safe and wear his full webbing and big pack as well as carrying his kitbag. That meant blancoing his webbing and polishing the brasses. When he had finished he felt very proud of his efforts as he looked at himself in the full-length mirror in his mum and dad's bedroom.

Bright and early the next morning, with his travel warrant and travelling instructions safely in his pocket, he set off to the station, enjoying the admiring glances of his fellow travellers.

6.   On the Job

His train journey was non-eventful and Bob finally arrived at the Guardroom of RAF Brister where an SP with a slight grin on his face directed him to Station Headquarters. An airman in battledress and a leather jerkin was just about to get on a bike outside the building when Bob arrived.

"Just come from training then?" said the lad.

"Yes," said Bob. "How did you know?"

"Nobody dresses like that around here mate, unless they are on jankers or straight from training."

Bob was not quite sure what to think, but he had quite a conversation with this "old hand" who proved to be an MT driver and quite a friendly sort. He directed Bob where to go and gave him a brief idea of what went on at Brister.

Having signed all the papers, been to Pay Accounts and the Orderly Room, which Bob gathered was the hub of the camp, the Corporal in charge of the Orderly Room told an SAC to take Bob to his billet and then to Stores to collect his bedding.

The billet turned out to be a two-storey brick building divided into four large rooms, two on each floor. His guide took him to his room on the top floor and found him an empty bed space. There were about eight beds on each side of the room, but as it was mid-afternoon there was nobody about. This was a new experience for Bob, who had been used to wooden huts since he joined the RAF. The other difference was that the room seemed more "lived-in", without the clinical atmosphere he was used to. He dumped his kit on the bed and his guide took him to the stores to collect his five blankets, two sheets and a pillow slip, and then helped him carry it back to his room.

When he got back, there was a lad lying on one of the beds reading the paper and when Bob was putting his clothes away he got up and came over and sat on the next bed. He introduced himself as Paddy and said he had just got back from a "job" and was waiting for mealtime. He gave Bob a hand to sort himself out and said he would show him the Airman's Mess and introduce him to the rest of the lads. Bob managed to tidy all his clothes away and make up his bed pack while they were waiting for the Mess to open and he took stock of the billet.

"Straight from training then?"

Two main things stood out a mile, there was the good old coke stove, the mainstay of RAF life, in the centre of the room although this one was a nice shade of cream enamel instead of the usual black lead, and Bob's newly manufactured bed pack was the only one in the whole room, the rest of the beds being neatly made and ready to get into. Paddy explained that the only time you made your bed pack up was if there was going to be a rare pre-planned room inspection, and although most of the beds were made up, a lot of their occupants were not actually on camp, but were away on a job somewhere. Bob also noticed that the floor was the usual brown lino, but instead of the highly polished gleam that he was used to, this one had a soft sheen. Bob felt he was going to like it here.

Bob and Paddy went off to the Mess and once again Bob got a pleasant surprise, the atmosphere was completely different to anything he was used to, with small groups spread around the room instead of whole huts or courses sitting together. Even the food looked and tasted like the real thing, with the people serving it seeming to want to be there rather than having to do it as a punishment. They sat at a table with three or four others, one of whom said he was from the Maintenance Unit Admin and he told Bob he would be joining the Salvage and Transportation Section.

Back at the their billet Bob was introduced to the rest of the inhabitants and, as Paddy had told him, even though there were around sixteen beds in the room there were only around nine people in residence at the moment. Three of those were Junior Technicians who were all ex Boy Entrants and it was immediately obvious that they were the ones to go to for advice. In fact, they, together with a young SAC, had formed a skiffle group with a guitar, tea chest double bass and a washboard, the SAC providing the vocals. Paddy explained that, as they were different trades, it was not that often they were all back at base at the same time, so tonight was a bit of an occasion. Bob enjoyed their amateur rendition of "Freight Train" and other country and western numbers and before he knew it people had started to turn in and it was gone 11.00pm. As he lay in bed, wondering who he could dream of, he thought to himself that this really was a different Air Force and one he thought he was even going to enjoy.

*"You do **not** salute bus drivers, coppers or security guards."*

The next day he was back down to SHQ to find out where he should be working and they confirmed he was indeed going to join the Aircraft Salvage and Transportation Section (AS&TS) and he was given directions to their hangar.

He found the right hangar and someone directed him to the Section Office. The hangar was full of aircraft, most of them with their wings removed and there was a general smell of new paint. The flight office was on one side of the hangar, behind a heavy steel door which was open. Bob entered the office to find a Flight Sergeant behind the desk who introduced himself as Flight Sergeant Meakin. The Flight Sergeant welcomed him to the AS&TS flight of 99 MU and explained "What we do for a living" which, he said, was to salvage crashed aircraft, transport aircraft and prepare and display exhibition aircraft. He then took him into the adjoining office to meet the officer in charge of the section, Flight Lieutenant Bronowski. This was all very new to Bob and, even though everyone still saluted officers, they seemed to be real people instead of the people on a pedestal he had been used to. Flt Sgt Meakin then handed Bob over to Corporal Jenkins and said Bob would be working in his work gang for the time being.

Corporal Jenkins (call me Mac) then said Bob would need to draw a toolbox and protective clothing from stores and sent him off with an MT driver to collect a vehicle and then get his equipment from the stores. His toolbox turned out to be full of tools and weigh about fifty or sixty pounds. He duly signed for the box and each of its contents, together with a waterproof over jacket, denim overalls, leather jerkin and heavyweight gloves.

When he got back to the hanger Mac Jenkins asked him if he had done any paint spraying. Bob said he hadn't.

"Now's your chance to learn," said Mac. "Give Lofty a hand on the Spitfire."

And so started Bob's career as an Engine Mechanic with 99 MU. Lofty showed him how to rub the old paint down with "wet and dry paper" and how to mask off the aircraft markings and camouflage.

After an hour or so someone shouted "Naafi Up!" and a general exodus was made through the hanger door, but only as far as the brown Naafi van that was parked outside. Bob and Lofty joined the queue and Bob realised that if he bought a cup of tea he had nothing to put it in. Lofty explained that he could buy a mug from the girl in the van and he should then keep it in his tool box. So Bob then paid out 2s-9d; two shillings for the mug, threepence for the tea and sixpence for a cheese roll, and followed Lofty back into the "Crew Room", which was next door to the Flight Office.

As they opened the door, a thick fog of cigarette smoke met them, much worse than the London "Smogs" that Bob had seen. Peering through the gloom he could make out a room about twelve feet by ten with a small, single fixed and barred window at the end. Round the walls were benches, now crowded with all ranks from lowly AC1s to Corporals, and in the centre was an oblong bare wooden table. Bob and Lofty squeezed onto a bench and ate their lunch. Bob looked around the room, which at some stage had been painted cream, but thanks to a few thousand cigarettes was now nicotine brown. Fixed to the walls were postcards of the kind you would not send to your maiden aunt and on one wall was a virtually undecipherable copy of what to do in case of fire.

'No fire could possibly burn in this room,' thought Bob. 'Fires need oxygen and there certainly is none in here.'

After about 15 minutes, a sergeant poked his head round the door and said "Naafi break over lads," upon which everyone filed out of the room and back to their tasks.

All this was completely alien to Bob; there was no shouting, no lining people up, everyone had their job to do and they just got on with it.

He spent the rest of the week smoothing down the many layers of paint applied to the Spitfire over the years. Bob learnt that this particular aircraft was one of the unit's display aircraft and was most certainly not airworthy. They were now preparing it for display later in the year and although it was not airworthy it had to appear to be so, with no dents, scratches or missing visible bolts or fasteners. The hanger was full of similar aircraft, a Hurricane, a Vampire and Bob's old friend a Meteor, some all ready for display, others in various stages of repair or painting.

The rest of the hangar was taken up with pieces of equipment of all shapes and sizes, but all painted bright blue. When Bob asked Lofty what these were, he was told they were pieces of Ground Equipment that were used to assemble and dismantle various types of aircraft and that he would eventually get to know which item to use for which job.

The only items not painted blue were some oblong wooden boxes, about six feet long, that resembled the front of a mouth organ. Lying beside these were some long, square wooden poles, wrapped in padding.

"What on earth are those?" asked Bob.

"The boxes are called "egg boxes" and the poles are "egg poles," said Lofty. "You put the egg box flat on the floor and put an egg pole into one of the holes so that it stands upright. You can then stand something like a wing or tailplane upright against the pole and put a second pole the other side to stop it falling over. We use them for storing and transporting parts of aircraft."

Bob was looking forward to getting stuck into a real job, such as transporting one of the aircraft, assembling it for display and then repeating the process and returning it to storage. As it turned out, he did not have long to wait, although the job was not going to be exactly what he had imagined.

The evenings were generally relaxed affairs. With no equipment to clean and polish and no swotting for exams, Bob was free to join the skiffle group, go to the Naafi, the Astra cinema or go into the local town. RAF Brister was built in two halves, with a busy road in between the two sites. On one side of the road was the guardroom, SHQ and all the workshops, hangars and airfield. The site on the other side of the road housed the accommodation blocks, cinema, Naafi and Mess. Therefore, although there were no restrictions on what they did or where they went outside of normal working hours, this set-up was very attractive because it meant that after a night out in the town they did not have to go past the Guardroom on their way back, with some power-hungry "Snowdrop" waiting to hassle them.

Bob found out that he could buy a "Forces Weekend Return" railway ticket for 27s 6d that took him most of the way home, there being a train from Brister station at ten past five on Friday evenings. This meant that if they finished work at 4.30 as usual on Friday, he could just make the train. The return train was just before 8.30 on Sunday evening, so he could have a nice long weekend at home if he wanted to.

It was after a weekend at home that he found himself on his first "job". Six of them were relaxing in their billet at about 11.00pm when one of their Sergeants came in and said that five of them would be going out at 6.30 the next morning. A large transport plane had come to grief on landing at Heathrow and there would be three "gangs" going down there. Bob was to be on his (Sgt Baynard)'s gang. They all asked Sgt Baynard what had happened, but he said the incident had only just taken place and he did not know too much about it. They were to assemble in their hanger at 6.15 in the morning and they would be briefed then. They should take their toolboxes and overnight kit.

Because there were about twenty five of them on the job, they were treated to an RAF coach instead of the usual three-tonner, their toolboxes and kit travelling in an Austin one tonner. They were told they would be staying at an Army camp about ten miles from London Airport, but they would be going straight to Heathrow initially. They were told that a large RAF aircraft had crashed short of the runway, with the unfortunate loss of three of the five crew. Bob wondered how his newly-acquired engineering skills would be used.

When they arrived on site it was immediately obvious that his new skills would certainly *not* be required on this occasion, because the aircraft was just a mass of broken, largely unrecognisable pieces of metal. They were divided into their gangs and then addressed by a group of civilians, who introduced themselves as members of the Air Investigation Branch (AIB). They explained that every single piece of metal was important and it was important not to damage them further. All the crash material was to be taken to Farnborough and laid out in a hanger, with each piece being placed on the floor in as close a position as possible to its original position on the aircraft.

A line of long, low-loader trailers, which Bob discovered were known as "Queen Marys" were waiting, together with a couple of mobile cranes. They had to load the aircraft engines and tail fin – still largely in one piece – first. This was so that these parts could be used as locating pieces when laying out the rest of the salvage, but they also needed to dispense with the cranes as soon as possible as they were directly under the runway approach.

Bob was told to work with Lofty and, if he had any doubts about identifying anything, he should ask one of the AIB men. Obviously, all the others had previous experience of fatal crashes and Bob was not sure how he would handle the situation, even though he was assured the medics had removed the unfortunate victims. As time passed, the mood was sombre, but with the occasional light hearted banter. Bob was to discover that this was not disrespect, but people's way of dealing with the situation.

At one stage Lofty said "Watch this…" He picked up a piece of twig about two inches long, walked over to group of three people and said in a loud voice, "Do you think this is a finger?" One of the three started to buckle at the knees and his two colleagues grabbed him. Lofty then said, "Sorry about that, I wasn't sure." The response from the three was not friendly and Lofty took refuge behind one of the cranes. Lofty later explained that the wobbly knee'd person was Ted Stanton, who was well known for his fear of finding human parts.

The job took them four days, working from dawn till dusk, in order to clear the airport approach path. They were happy to spend as much time as possible on site because the Army camp really was the pits; the food was totally inedible and the hut they were housed in looked as though it had not been used since the war – the 1918 war! They eat during the day at the BOAC canteen, which by comparison was pure luxury;

they could identify the food by sight and taste and Bob found the Air Stewardesses quite tasty as well.

Eventually they cleared the site and it was back to Brister and painting. Bob found he quite enjoyed preparing the aircraft and they eventually let him loose with a spray gun. This turned out to be a good move, because Bob became quite good at spraying and this was going to earn him a few brownie points later when senior NCOs decided their cars needed some bodywork attention.

They managed to complete the painting of the Spitfire just in time for it to be loaded for an exhibition in Chester, the exhibition was in aid of the Chester Wings Day appeal and an Avon engine would be accompanying the Spitfire for the three day exhibition.

Bob was told he would be going on the job, together with John Morris and Corporal Jock Miller. Bob and Corporal Miller travelled in the Queen Mary with the aircraft and engine and John Morris travelled in the Coles crane that was going with them. They loaded the Spitfire themselves and Cpl Miller explained that he was the official "Second Man". He said the driver was responsible for the safety of the vehicle, but the "Second Man" was responsible for the load. This meant he had a load sheet, onto which he had to record regular checks on the stability and safety of the load. This entailed checking the tightness of securing strops and ropes and ensuring any packing and tarpaulins were in place and secure.

They set off north, using main roads wherever possible, due to the length of the vehicle, but even the main roads were extremely narrow in places and, as all commercial vehicles were restricted to thirty miles an hour, a queue of cars soon built up behind them. After about thirty minutes, Corporal

Miller asked the driver to pull into a lay-by, as he needed to check the load. He explained that the load "bedded down" in the first few miles and he would probably need to tighten the restraining ropes and strops.

This job done, they were back on the road, starting their own traffic congestion once again, but Bob noticed that nobody hooted them and indeed when cars finally got past, they usually gave a toot and a wave. Jock Miller explained that this was the "Spitfire effect" and not to expect the same treatment if they were carrying a nondescript load covered in a tarpaulin.

Bob then asked Jock Miller where they would be sleeping and Jock said that, as there were no suitable Army or RAF stations nearby, they would stay in a B&B. He had been to Chester before and he knew of a suitable place to stay, but he explained that Bob would need to pay for his own "digs" and then claim it back.

"Have you got a 1771?" asked Jock.

"What on earth is that?" replied Bob.

"I can see that you need some training in the way you need to live on this MU," said Jock, and he went on to explain the way they made sure they did not lose money on their many jobs away from Brister – and even make a few bob where possible.

Jock explained that Bob needed to go to Pay Accounts and get some blank forms known as F1771s, these were used to claim back your out of pocket expenses and he should always make sure he had a supply. He then explained they were allowed to claim 21 shillings a night for the first seven nights away – this was known as *Rate 1*; after that it reduced to *Rate 2*, which was 17/6d per night. There were other fixed allowances for meals. Jock then explained that you simply fixed the accommodation receipts to the F1771 and gave it to Pay Accounts.

"So how do you make money then?" asked Bob.

"Well lad, when you get to know the places we stay in, they will charge you 18 bob and give you a receipt for 21 bob, or you try to stop at an Army or RAF station and still claim on your 1771. No one ever checks, and you do not need receipts for meal breaks, so we stop at cheap transport cafés and put up with some pretty rough grub and save a bob or two to pay for our beer in the evening."

Bob could not really get his head round all this. Here was a corporal he was calling by his Christian name, telling him how to fiddle a bit of extra cash; a lot different to Corporals Jones and Atkins of a previous time. Bob thought this might be a bit of a set-up, but he asked the driver of the Queen Mary and he replied, "Why do you think everyone wants to get out onto a job? What Jock has said is what we all do. Just join the gang mate!" So Bob decided that was exactly what he was going to do.

They arrived in Chester and Jock said if they drove into a transport café car park they could drop the trailer, leave Bob to guard it and he and the driver would go off in the "donkey" to sort out the accommodation. They would start erecting the Spitfire first thing in the morning.

After about an hour they were back and said everything was arranged. They were going to leave the Queen Mary in a Police car park and the digs were only a short walk away.

They eventually arrived at a private house, painted bright yellow, and the landlady introduced herself as "Mrs Bucknell, dear." Mrs Bucknell was a bit over-dressed and definitely trying to look younger than her years. There did not seem to be a Mr Bucknell and she explained she enjoyed looking after

"You RAF boys", along with actors appearing at the local theatre. She cooked them a very nice evening meal and it was not until they were going to bed that Bob got concerned. As he was about to go upstairs she said, "Goodnight dear, would you like a hot water bottle?" The smile on her face and the fact that it was the height of summer made Bob decline the offer.

The night passed without incident, although Bob was sure he heard someone creeping about just before he dropped off and wondered just who was cuddling the "hot water bottle". None of the gang would own up to it the next day, but Bob thought Jock looked a bit tired.

They arrived at the square where the Spitfire was to be displayed and started to unload their toolboxes, jacks and trestles. They lined the fuselage up on its trestles and placed the strops round the left wing, ready to join it to the fuselage. Although the crane was taking the weight of the wing ("We call it a mainplane, lad") Bob soon found that two of them spent half an hour with it on their backs, supporting, lifting and twisting the damn thing, while Jock tried to fit the holding bolts. Obviously Bob was trained as an engine mechanic but he could not believe that the wing of a fighter aircraft was only held on by three bolts. Jock explained that the majority of aircraft, even bombers, only had three attachment bolts, two large tapered ones at the top and bottom of the mainspar and a smaller one at the rear spar. Jock also explained that no matter how much grease you put on the exhibition aircraft bolts, they always jammed if a dignitary was watching. Today was no exception.

They eventually managed to fit both wings and lower the undercarriage. Again, this involved putting their backs under the wheel and taking the weight, while Jock released the "wheel-up" lock. On an airworthy aircraft, of course, this would be done using the hydraulics or compressed air, but if you only had a few hours to erect or dismantle the aircraft, then it had to be done the quick way.

So with the aircraft now on its feet, the only thing left was the laborious task of fitting the shaped fillets that cover the joint between the wings and the fuselage. As the aircraft was on public view, there was no shortcut for this task and many screws and fasteners had to be in place on each fillet. It was then just a matter of a quick final clean-up to remove greasy handprints and the Spitfire looked as though it had just landed.

At this stage the RAF recruitment team took over. One of the 99 MU lads had to stay on site while the exhibition was open, but the rest had time to themselves for the three days of the exhibition and then it was time to reverse the process and dismantle the aircraft.

While they were on duty at the exhibition they were not encouraged to spend time with the public, their working blue attire was not the image the RAF wished to promote, but while Bob was doing his duty day he managed to chat up quite a few local people, mostly girls of course.

One girl was quite a tall blonde, who explained that she was Swedish and was a tour guide. Her party of tourists were spending the day shopping and she had the day off. Bob did his, "I am normally called on to do all the highly technical jobs" chat-up line and the girl, who said her name was Ingrid (didn't they all), seemed to be quite impressed. They chatted for a long time and then agreed to meet later in the evening. Her tour was moving on to the Lake District the next day but she was free this evening.

Bob finished his shift, had a quick meal back at the B&B and a bath (which cost him an extra 5 shillings). He managed to borrow a decent shirt from one of the other lads and aftershave from Jock. He then set off for his rendezvous with the rather sexy Ingrid...

Bob was pleasantly surprised when Ingrid turned up for their date and they set off to find a quiet pub. They had a quiet drink and chatted about their jobs and Ingrid told him she was only being a tour guide while she waited to go to university ... but then Bob had told *her* that he normally carried out all the highly technical jobs on aircraft.

Oh what a tangled web we weave...

Ingrid then said she did not really like pubs and why didn't they go for a walk. Now this was the 1950s, but the reputation of girls in Sweden was already well known, so Bob was well up for this. They walked through the town centre, past the cathedral and found a nice grassy bank overlooking the River Dee. Bob suggested they should sit and have a breather and Ingrid agreed. The chat soon turned to more personal matters and it started to become obvious why Swedish girls had their reputation. They were soon becoming more familiar, but this was a fairly public place and Bob suggested they move somewhere a little bit more private. Ingrid said OK and they set off, Bob getting a nice warm feeling in certain areas. As they turned a corner on the footpath, a voice said "Hallå Ingrid," followed by a lengthy and earnest conversation in what Bob took to be Swedish, during which Ingrid's face became quite serious.

Ingrid then said to Bob, "I am sorry Bob, but one of my party has been taken ill and I am going back to our hotel to make arrangements. I was looking forward to getting to know you better, but I am afraid it has to be goodbye." She gave him a very passionate kiss that did nothing to cool the already overheated parts of his anatomy and then she was off, never to be seen again.

When he got back to the B&B he was given the third degree by the lads and they seemed to feel genuinely sorry for him. Even Jock was sympathetic and said, "Never mind Bob, wait until you go on a job to Norfolk; the Swedes there all speak English!" Being a corporal had not improved Jock's manners.

The rest of the Chester job passed without incident and soon, after removing dozens of screws and heaving the undercarriage up until it locked, they were back on the road to Brister.

In between painting ground equipment, sweeping the hanger floor and the odd "private job" on NCOs cars, Bob managed to get to know a few of the local girls. This made the evenings more enjoyable and even added to his knowledge of all things female. His regular meetings with the local "talent" were, however, put in the shade by a lad called Lofty Davis, who had a bed half way down the billet. It was obvious to the lads that he had a girl locally, because he would go out every night and return around midnight or later.

Obviously, the lads were envious of his imagined activities, but the problem was his return in the small hours. He would come in, turn the lights on and make as much noise as was humanly possible by someone undressing and getting into bed. This was getting on their nerves and one wet night they had a "conference" about the situation.

"We need to teach him a lesson," Brian Newman said, "and maybe the best way for him to take the hint is for us to play a practical joke on him. What about an apple-pie bed?"

This was thought to be a bit tame and childish.

"As he is seeing a woman, maybe we should involve sex in some way," Brummy Taylor chipped in. "Has anyone got a condom?"

A condom (unused) was produced and then some Brylcreem, which was easy to find in the 50s RAF. Brummy then blew the condom up to stretch it, placed some Brylcreem and a drop of water inside it, and tied the end.

They then placed it in one of Lofty's uniform socks and waited for the reaction when he got dressed in the morning.

He certainly reacted, but not in the way they expected. There was much shouting and name-calling, but then silence. Lofty would not speak to anyone for a couple of weeks, but unfortunately the nightly disturbance carried on.

Time for further action, they decided.

This time they used a condom again and stuffed it with a carrot they had got from the cookhouse. Around the end they tied some feathers from a pillow that had seen better days. As they were on the top floor of the accommodation block, their room had wooden rafters along the roof; fortunately one of these was above Lofty's bed. They then suspended their little toy above his bed on a piece of string that ended at Brummy's bed, the idea being that after Lofty put the lights out they would lower the customised carrot until it touched his head.

Sure enough, at 12.15 Lofty came in with his usual crash, bang, wallop entrance and eventually put out the lights. After a short time, to allow his eyes to get used to the dark, Brummy gently lowered the contraption onto Lofty's bed.

At first, nothing happened, but then there was an almighty shout and the lights came on. A side of Lofty they had not seen before then became apparent as he ranted and raved for a good half-hour. He definitely was *not* amused!

Bob decided that the best way to sort this out would be to tell Lofty why they played these tricks on him, so he said, "We only did this, Lofty, because we are fed-up with you waking us up every night after you have been out with your girlfriend."

"For your information," Lofty said, "I do not have a girlfriend. I am not really interested in girls."

'Oh-oh,' thought Bob.

"As a matter of fact, I work for a local charity in the town every night. Your tricks were very childish, but I understand now why you did it and I am sorry. I will try to be quieter in future." By this time it was 2 am and everyone agreed to call a truce and get some sleep.

True to his promise, Lofty bought himself a torch, swapped beds with someone just inside the door and was as quiet as a church mouse from then on. Weeks later, someone discovered that Lofty was actually a Samaritans volunteer. They all felt a bit ashamed of their actions, although it had given them all a good laugh at the time. Even Lofty laughed about it afterwards.

Bob had just got back from Oxford, where they had taken the Vampire and Meteor aircraft for a recruitment exhibition. He still had scratches around both forearms to prove it, because he had foolishly volunteered to help the Airframe people out by fitting the tail booms on the Vampire. The small access panels that you had to use to fit the bolts that joined the tail boom to the fuselage section had scratched his arms to pieces. The airframe lads knew this and were obviously very happy to let him volunteer.

He was called into the Section Office and Flight Sergeant Meakin said he had a special job for him for the next two weeks or so.

"There is an exercise being held up in Northumberland, involving aircraft of the American Air Force, the Dutch and the RAF. All the RAF aircraft will come from the auxiliary squadrons and the ground crew from reservists doing their yearly summer camp. They need some serving airmen to give them support and as you are still fresh from training I am sending you."

Bob was not sure what to say. It sounded exciting, getting to work on real aircraft, but as he had no real experience, could he cope? But Chiefy (Flight Sergeants were always called Chiefy – after Chief Technician – as long as there was no objection) had said it was their 'summer camp', so perhaps it would be fun. He collected his travel warrant and the next day was off to the North East.

He arrived at RAF Huckleton and booked into Station Headquarters. He was directed to the hut that would be his home for two weeks and settled himself into a bedspace. In due course a Sergeant arrived and said he was in charge of the people that would be sleeping in the hut and would then be working out on the airfield on the "Readiness Stand". He said that Bob was the first to arrive, but the others would be arriving over the next day, they were reservists and some of them would have been nowhere near an aircraft for a couple of years, so he expected Bob to support them.

'Blimey,' thought Bob, 'talk about the blind leading the blind.'

Eventually his roommates started to arrive and it soon became clear to Bob that they were taking on the appearance of the Barmy Army. Because they had been nowhere near any RAF establishment for at least a year, their uniforms either did not fit or had been thrown away. Some had uniform jackets and their own trousers; some had black shoes and others brown, and their hats, if they had one, varied from berets to peaked or forage caps.

'It's no wonder they are going to hide us on the airfield,' thought Bob.

They were eventually issued with denim overalls, however, which served to hide a multitude of sins.

They were told the exercise would start the following day, but that a truck would take them out to the airfield a bit later to show them where they would be working. They were to be housed during the day in a marquee at the end of the runway, close to the hard-standing that would accommodate their aircraft. The aircraft were going to be Meteors of 600 Squadron, Royal Auxiliary Air Force.

It was a beautiful sunny day, but the airfield was, like most airfields, very windy, the wind coming straight off the North Sea. It was explained that their squadron was one of the defending squadrons and the Sabres of the Americans and Dutch would be the attackers, these aircraft being based elsewhere in England and Holland. The job Bob and the Barmy Army would be doing was to look after 600 Squadron's aircraft and get them airborne as quickly as possible when they were instructed to scramble. Sometimes the pilots would be sitting in their aircraft and at other times they would be in the marquee on standby.

They would be collected from their billet at dawn and taken to the airfield and the marquee, which would be their home until dusk. This would last for ten days and then they would return to their homes – or Brister in Bob's case. Meals would be provided, including breakfast, in the marquee and toilet facilities were also available. These toilets turned out to be two Elsan buckets, surrounded by six-foot high hessian panels, supported by wooden poles.

The aircraft were already in position and the Sergeant gave them instructions on their duties. One or two of the reservists had carried out this duty when they did their National Service, so the Sergeant did not spend too long on the instructions.

There were going to be two men allocated to each aircraft and their job was to check that all control surfaces were free, strap the pilot in (minding the ejector seat), man the fire extinguishers, remove the chocks, remove the TrolleyAcc power supply to the aircraft and remove the communication cable that connected the aircraft and the control tower.

This all sounded very simple and Bob was sure they would soon get it down to a fine art. However, when the morning came, it was raining, the aircraft were "live" and it was a totally different ball game. Bob had never seen a pilot's collection of straps, pipes and cables. His first effort at strapping the pilot in was a complete disaster and he was subjected to just about every swear word he had ever heard, as well as some he hadn't, all delivered in a cut-glass Oxford accent! That was the first problem and then he realised that the TrolleyAcc connection could not be removed until the engines were running, and it was sited just in front of the port engine. (They had all heard horror stories of erks being sucked into engines!)

The final problem was the comms cable, as Bob discovered the first time he removed one. This plugged into the bottom of the fuselage, right between the two engines and, like the front plug, could only be removed when the engines were running. Bob had to crawl forward along the line of the rear fuselage, crouch under the plug and wait for his mate to get the thumbs-up from the pilot. When he got the thumbs-up he had to remove the plug, show it to his mate and return the way he had come.

This all went according to plan but, as soon clearance for takeoff had been granted, Bob realised that the pilot's throttle hand worked a lot quicker than his legs. As full power thrust the aircraft in one direction, Bob becoming airborne in the other. As he sailed through the air he made a mental note to run a bit quicker next time and not to show the plug to his mate until he was as far as possible from the engines!

The exercise continued for the next few days, with just the occasional USAAF Sabre performing a low level "beat-up" of their aircraft and marquee. Bob soon realised that when this happened the best place to be was outside the marquee, the American pilots not having a very good reputation for accurate flying, as Bob was to find out later.

Their marquee was positioned on the grass in the corner between the main runway and a taxiway. This taxiway was being used to park the squadron aircraft that were not on readiness or were being serviced. Behind the marquee and the parked aircraft were the two ablution enclosures, far enough away from the marquee to prevent any air pollution, but close enough to keep an eye on.

After a particularly heavy night in the local pub, one of the reservists decided that sunset was too long to wait to get back to a proper "waste disposal unit" and that he would have to take a seat on one of the venerable Elsans. He was about half way through the *Daily Mirror* when they decided to carry out engine runs on one of the Meteors with its back to his hideaway. Not only did they run the engines, but for whatever reason they did it at full power. The wooden poles of his emporium valiantly withstood the blast briefly but then surrendered and with a clatter, disappeared into the distance.

Normal private facilities were provided.

The poor fellow inside was made of heavier material, even though he was now a little lighter than previously, and remained proudly sitting on his throne for all the world to see. He now had a problem of course… should he complete his toilet process? – having had the presence of mind to grab the toilet roll before it disappeared – or should he simply whip his trousers up and run?

Unfortunately Bob's aircraft was told to scramble at that moment and he never did find out how the poor chap resolved his problem.

The exercise finished without any further entertainment and Bob was glad to get back to proper accommodation. Although it was the middle of the summer, he found that the top of a hill in Northumbria at six am is not the warmest place to be, even on the hottest days. RAF Huckleton was home to a target-towing flight of converted Blenheim light bombers, the mid-turret and gunner having been replaced by a winch mechanism and its operator. It was decided that the Americans would take advantage of this facility and a group of their Sabres stayed behind for some target practise.

However, because of the exercise, many of the regular Blenheim ground and aircrew had taken their annual leave, with the result that although they had enough cockpit crews, they were short of winch operators.

Bob had three days before he was due to return to Brister and the thought of a chance to fly and to earn the grand sum of sixpence a day flying pay, appealed to him. He volunteered to become a temporary winch operator, even though he had no idea what it entailed.

He reported to the hanger and was given a flying suit and shown the seat he would occupy in the aircraft. It was explained that the suit was needed because the Blenheim was a notoriously cold and draughty aircraft, in addition to which it would provide some padding between him and the hard metal so-called seat. He was given intensive instruction on the job he was going to do, with particular emphasis being placed on the emergency handle, which he would have to pull if the pilot instructed him to 'cut loose the target'.

It was at this stage that Bob fully realised just what target towing was all about. He found the whole process to be a bit butt clenching! The Blenheim towed a piece of material that was about twenty five feet long and four feet high, on a long cable which was winched in and out by Bob. Viewed from the side, this piece of material represented an aircraft fuselage but, of course, being just a flat piece of material it did not present a target from above or below – and definitely not from the rear.

Pilots were under strict instructions to only fire from the broadside position and this is exactly what happened on

Bob's first two flights. The target was a long way behind the Blenheim and, although the flight was noisy, bumpy and cold, he really enjoyed it.

Then came the third flight and Bob should have realised there would be problems when he saw the guide dog sitting in the rear cockpit of the Sabre. The American pilot executed a sharp bank to the left and lined up behind the target and suddenly Bob realised he had opened fire. Now the cable was extended to its full length, but the range of the guns on the Sabre far exceeded this and they were in real danger of being shot down by some trigger-happy Yank.

Bob shouted over the intercom, "Blimey Sir, the idiot is firing at us from behind!"

The one word reply had to do with human reproduction and then the command came to cut the cable, which Bob could not do quickly enough. There followed an extremely animated conversation between the pilot and what Bob assumed to be the Americans as they made their way back to Huckleton. When they landed, the pilot took off at a trot for the CO's office. So there ended Bob's first experience of both flying and the Americans; the first mostly pleasant and the latter most definitely not so.

The rest of his time at Huckleton passed without further incident and Bob made his way back to Brister, where he knew he could have a pint or two on his stories of life on a squadron.

When he got back there were rumours flying around that the RAF Regiment was planning to attack the camp as part of an exercise aimed at improving security throughout the RAF. As a result they had doubled the people being called for guard and fire picket duty and Bob was therefore not at all surprised to see his name on the guard duty roster. He just hoped he was called out on a job before the due date, as he did not fancy spending all night patrolling the airfield boundary and aircraft dump with just a baseball bat for company.

No such luck. He found himself with Alan Payne, an armourer, on guard duty inside the Station Armoury. They had to spend four hours in the Armoury and then four hours in the guardroom. Alan was spending his four hours in the guardroom, leaving Bob in charge of the Armoury, he had also left his bicycle leaning against the building, ready for the morning. Bob was just settling down in the scruffy but comfortable armchair used by the armourers when there was a loud banging at the door. Bob opened the spy hatch in the door and a Corporal said, "The Guardroom have instructed that your bike must be taken inside the Armoury for security reasons". Bob replied that he would do it shortly, but had no intention of doing so. It was not his bike anyway. An hour later the Corporal was back, but by this time Bob had got his head down and he was not going outside for anyone.

The following morning, he was sleeping off his night duty and was woken to be told that the C.O. wanted to see him right away. As he dressed, Bob was wondering what the penalty was for disobeying an order issued by the Guardroom. He was taken into the CO's office and as he entered the building, the Corporal from the previous evening was just leaving. It was obvious to Bob that he had just been giving the CO the full story of how Bob had disobeyed an order.

When he arrived in front of the CO he was met with a smile and told to stand easy.

"Congratulations Wilson," said the CO. "Your quick thinking last night prevented the RAF Regiment from carrying out a devious raid on the Station and saved us all from having very red faces."

Now Bob was not altogether 'with it', due to lack of sleep, and his brain went into overdrive, trying to remember just what brave deed he had done last night. He couldn't think of anything, so he just nodded and smiled.

The CO went on to explain that knocking on the Armoury door was part of the plan to get Bob outside the building to take the bike inside. While he was doing this, the six Regiment "enemy", who had been hiding round the corner, would rush in, capture the building and hold the Station to ransom.

With his brain now in reheat, Bob said, "Thank you Sir. I thought that was the best thing to do!"

It was shortly after this incident that Bob was told he had been promoted to Leading Aircraftsman. He spent all one weekend stitching his rank badges onto his two jackets and his greatcoat; he thought about putting them on his pyjamas but decided not to. The promotion was probably due anyway, but Bob liked to think it was down to his heroic stand in the Armoury and he could not wait to go home in uniform and show off his newly-achieved status.

The next three weeks or so were spent at Brister, preparing aircraft for the big exhibition of the year, the Battle of Britain displays around the country. During this time, Bob got to know a bit more about some of his fellow erks, both National Service and regular. Most of them were average lads of 18 to 20, with a few "old timers" that had decided to make the RAF their home and were not really interested in promotion.

It was a difficult life for those that could not fit in or could or would not "follow the flow". One such person was LAC John Smith. He was supposedly a high flyer in the media industry before he was called for National Service.

Unfortunately, he was a square peg in every RAF round hole and did not mix with anyone. He had some extremely weird habits. On more than one occasion Bob saw him having a wet shave in the Ablutions, fully dressed in jacket, collar and tie, with his beret planted firmly, like a pancake, on his head. The crowning glory was the smouldering pipe, clenched firmly between his teeth! Because of his strange behaviour and lack of mates John Smith was subjected to a lot a practical jokes and mickey-taking. One day Bob went back to the billet to collect his F 1771 and found him cramming his belongings into his kit bag.

"Going on leave?" asked Bob.

"No," replied John. "I am leaving."

He obviously had said more than his quota for the day so Bob did not ask the reason. It was learnt later that he had been medically discharged

The other Section of 99 MU carried out heavy repairs on aircraft at the aircraft's home base. Damage resulting from "tail scrapes", ground collisions and wheels-up landings were repaired by this section. A Junior Technician had recently been posted into this section and it was said that he had re-mustered from the Army, which was not too unusual, but to have been a Captain in the Army and become an "other ranks" in the RAF certainly was. People wondered just what it was that he had been guilty of.

It soon became clear just what the problem had been because within a couple of weeks of his arrival a pair of outsize RAF issue WAAF's bloomers were found flying from the Station flagpole on the parade ground, evidently put there by this J/T and a few of his room-mates.

The first thing you can do is take those bloody knickers down.

In their billet it seems there was a poor unfortunate who could sleep for Britain, but in the process destroyed everyone else's chance of sleep with his snoring.

The accommodation blocks were along the side of the station parade ground. The parade ground was very rarely used, most parades being held on the aircraft parking area on the Technical side of the station, but despite this the station parade ground was the pride and joy of the Station Warrant Officer and was hallowed ground. You walked across it at your peril!

One night our nutty J/T decided that enough was enough and took his own action on the poor snorer. The next morning they were all treated to the spectacle of one sleeping and snoring airman safely tucked up in bed – in the middle of the parade ground!

The time had come to load the aircraft and ground equipment for the Battle of Britain displays and Bob never did hear the outcome of this latest display of Army humour.

Bob had been put on the gang that was going down to London to place around six aircraft on Horse Guards Parade to celebrate Battle of Britain Day. As well as the usual Spitfire and Hurricane they were taking a Hunter and Vampire and an aircraft from the RAF classic aircraft store at Wroughton as well as the Supermarine S6b float plane that won the Schneider Trophy in the 1930s, which had been borrowed from a Southampton museum. There were about six lads and a Chief Tech in the gang and they were allowed to take the caravan reserved for jobs where there was no local accommodation. This was used purely as a an office/mess room, the gang being billeted at a north London RAF station, although Bob had elected to travel home each night.

They erected the aircraft in a corner of Horse Guards Parade and parked the caravan close to a high brick wall at the edge. While it took all day to erect the main display aircraft, a couple of the MT drivers set about getting a brew on the go in the caravan. While they were having a tea break, Bob noticed two policemen standing by the wall and asked them if they wanted a cuppa.

"We will have to charge you tuppence a cup," said Trevor Biggs, "To cover our costs." The police agreed that this was fair and thereby started a profitable tradition that was to last for the Battle of Britain exhibitions of the next few years.

Bob asked the police if they were guarding the brick wall or just skiving.

"You do know what is on the other side of that wall don't you?" said one of them.

Bob said he did not.

"Well," he said, "your caravan is parked about six feet from the back garden wall of number ten Downing Street."

Bob realised now why two policemen were patrolling the wall twenty four hours a day. Each day from then on, police officers would appear from every corner to form a queue at the caravan at brew-up times, a bit like the homeless at a soup kitchen. The big difference, Bob thought, was that at least they were making a profit. It was a reciprocal arrangement in a way, because all the 99MU people were allowed to eat at New Scotland Yard, just the other side of Whitehall. The food was cheap, but not very inspiring, although it probably compared favourably with the tea the MT drivers sometimes came up with. This particular job was one all the lads enjoyed because, as well as being part of the bustle of London, they had grandstand views of Changing of the Guard. There were also a lot of young female tourists to entertain…

The Horse Guards job duly finished with a few new friendships made – mostly female – and with a few extra bob in the pocket, thanks to the "tea swindle". His next job in London did not happen until the Autumn, when Bob and Corporal "Tubby" Rogers had to take an aircraft that had been part of the recent Trans-Antarctic Expedition down to the Festival Hall for exhibition outside the hall, where Dr Vivien Fuchs was giving a lecture.

Tubby Rogers truly lived up to his name because he was a big lad. So big, in fact, that he could not get into the Guards type sentry box that was provided for their protection! They erected the light aircraft and, apart from guarding it day and night, their job was done for the week.

The doorman at the Festival Hall had a window that overlooked the aircraft and it did not take much persuasion for him to let Bob and Tubby in to spend the night in a couple of the performers' dressing rooms while he kept an eye on their aircraft. While they were at the Festival Hall, Frankie Vaughan was giving a concert in aid of his Boys Clubs and Field Marshal Montgomery attended a Remembrance Day Concert. They both passed through the stage door while Bob and Tubby were drinking the doorman's tea. Frankie Vaughan was very friendly and stopped for a chat, but Monty swept through without a word, which was just as well, as Bob had been lounging against the counter with his hat off and jacket undone when he suddenly appeared in the doorway.

While they were at the Festival Hall, the Shell Building was being built just across the road. At the time it was one of the tallest buildings in London. They were using one of the very tall tower cranes in its construction and Bob would watch the crane operator commence his fifteen minute climb up the ladder to his cabin at 8.30 each morning and then start back down again at 4.30 in the afternoon. Bob thought this must be the loneliest job in the world. His thoughts also turned to the supply of food, etc and disposal of the resulting waste products. This question was answered one day when he spied what looked like a bucket being lowered from the cabin on a long rope or cable. Not the sort of job to have if you were too fond of curry, Bob thought.

Life on 99MU continued with a good mix of jobs to keep them busy, these ranging from dealing with the results of "unscheduled landings" to local exhibitions in market towns across the South East of England. Bob was becoming aware of how little time he spent at Brister, having been there for some months and only seeing Brummy Wheeler two or three times – and Brummy slept in the next bed!

At least this meant he escaped from the usual parades and billet inspections, although this was a working Unit and these were few and far between anyway. The one parade that everything stopped for was the annual A.O.C's inspection, when the Air Commodore in charge of their Group would visit the station. This would mean practice parades and inspections for a couple of weeks prior to the visit and during this time only gangs on emergency jobs were allowed to leave Brister.

Their C.O. at this time was a red-faced Wing Commander with a short time left before retirement and the will to please the A.O.C come what may. This resulted in the Unit Stores being inundated with requests for replacement hats, jackets, ties, etc, because the Wing Commander considered the originals to be "Bloody scruffy". One poor J/T had to return three times to the Stores to replace his tie, each time the replacement not achieving the CO's blessing.

The A.O.C's parades were held on the tarmac between two hangers, out of sight of the Airfield Control Tower. The AOC was due to fly in, inspect a Guard of Honour beside the Control Tower then be driven to inspect the parade.

Tubby Rogers was considered to be a non-starter on the parade because the CO considered he would "Take up too much room." He was therefore posted on the corner of the hanger in order to warn the CO when the AOC was on his way.

The initial warm-up and preliminary inspections over, the CO had everyone standing easy, awaiting the AOC. Tubby suddenly shouted, "He is on his way Sir!" and promptly disappeared into the hanger out of sight.

"Parade, atten...tion!" bawled the CO.

The 'borrowed' RAF band struck up the RAF Marchpast and … the station dustcart drove round the corner!

People were still giggling when the AOC finally did arrive five minutes later. Needless to say, the CO was not one of them. Had he had a white shirt on, he would have looked like a walking RAF roundel with his bright red face and blue uniform.

The event went very well eventually and the usual "Well Done" signal was received from Group HQ and posted on noticeboards. By this time Bob was on a job in Suffolk, which entailed dismantling a Javelin fighter that had got entangled in some trees about five hundred yards from the end of the runway. The Javelin was a big, two seat, twin-engined, delta wing aircraft that had quite a short history in the RAF. It was liked by ground crews, but had a mixed reception from aircrew. It appeared that this particular aircraft had been reported by the pilot as having poor brake response when landing and it had been checked out and passed by the ground crew. On landing a few flights later the pilot only just managed to stop before the end of the runway and yet again it was checked and returned to service. On the very next flight it was obvious to the pilot that the problem was still there and while it was travelling at reasonable speed towards the end of the runway, he shut the fuel valves, and suggested he and his mate left the aircraft to it. They were both out on the wing as it travelled across the grass and jumped off before it entered the trees, self-preservation obviously being important to these gentlemen.

Having managed to avoid parades for most of his time at Brister, Bob was unlucky enough to get caught again only a few months after the AOC's visit. One weekend in November, Bob and three other lads were lounging around in the billet on one of their rare Saturdays on camp. The Duty Sergeant walked in and said he had been told to get a group of twenty or so Airmen together to represent RAF Brister at the Remembrance Day Parade in Oxford the next day. He was desperate to get enough men and said "You will volunteer won't you?" They were told it would only last around an hour and the local USAAF base had invited them back there afterwards.

They decided that it would be better than spending a boring Sunday lying on their beds and the visit to the USAAF base could be interesting, so against all Erk's rules they volunteered. They now had a problem; due to their nomadic lifestyle their kit tended to be spread around their Brister cupboards, their homes and their girlfriend's homes. This started them on a hunt to beg, steal or borrow the required equipment; greatcoats, webbing belts, Best Blue, including big hats and gloves-woollen. This exercise took up the rest of Saturday, at the end of which, provided they kept their greatcoats on, they would look reasonably smart. Removing their greatcoats would reveal trousers that were drooping round their knees, jackets with different rank insignia to their greatcoats and big hats stuffed with newspaper to keep them off their ears.

Sunday arrived and a coach took them to Oxford. On arrival at the parade start point they found themselves mixing with British Army Engineers, Infantry, a Royal Navy squad with their "fore & aft" hats and bum freezer uniforms and, putting everyone in the shade, the USAAF. These men were dressed in chrome helmets, smooth uniforms, brilliant white plastic webbing, white gaiters and what looked like baseball boots. 'Obviously,' thought Bob, 'their uniform designers are better at their jobs than their pilots.'

As if this was not demoralising enough, the Parade Officer placed the RAF Brister group just in front of the Americans in the parade and behind the British Infantry. Now it may not be realised but Infantry regiments march at twice the pace of the rest of Service Units and as the Infantry approached the Band and the Saluting Dais, the band increased their tempo. The Brister mob were finding it difficult enough to get everything in unison anyway, and the change in tempo certainly did not improve matters. To make matters worse, the Band Master obviously fancied his chances as a budding Victor Sylvester and the band broke into "When the Saints...." as the Americans approached.

At the end of the parade the lads gathered round the Sergeant and everyone was obviously embarrassed at their performance. They decided it would be better if they did not accept the invitation to the American Base and asked the Sergeant to pass on their regrets that they were, after all, a working unit and some of them had been called out on an emergency. The Sergeant got the coach driver to stop at a pub on their way back and they all did their best to forget the day's events.

Bob's view of the USAAF was tempered as time went on. The one incident that helped to change his view was during a particular job when they had to dismantle a transport aircraft on an RAF base in Gloucestershire, transport it to an RAF Station in Kent and re-erect it. Once the aircraft was dismantled it was loaded onto four Queen Marys and they set off for Kent. It was the middle of the winter, which made for an interesting journey in the ice and snow. They obviously needed to make two overnight stops; the problem was where can you park four fully loaded Queen Marys overnight? Now MT drivers are a pretty resourceful lot and they instantly dismissed the idea of an Army camp (on food grounds) or RAF bases ("We can't make money on there"). They therefore finished up on a USAAF base on the first night, where security was like nothing they had seen before. They were later to discover this was one of the bases that had a supply of nuclear bombs on site!

Having negotiated security and parked their vehicles, they were directed to their billet. How the other half lived! The building was bright and airy, there were curtains, bedside rugs and pure luxury – central heating.

They were told the cookhouse had finished the evening meal, but if they went along, "They will rustle up some chow for you guys."

Once again, the building was an eye-opener to the poor, downtrodden RAF lads. Everywhere was stainless steel and one wall was taken up by fridges and cold cabinets. No battered urns and chipped Formica for this Air Force. There were further surprises in store when they got to the servery. The Americans apologised that they had finished serving, but they had "hamburger" and they could rustle up some "fries". Hamburgers were a new thing to most of the lads but someone said they were round things made of minced meat that you eat them in a bun. But when the 'hamburger' was produced it was in an oblong dish around eighteen inches by twelve and three inches thick.

"How much would you guys like?" said the American, and proceeded to cut the hamburger into six-inch squares. To this was added a pile of freshly fried chips. They were in heaven! Afterwards they produced some apple pie and a large jug of cream for those who wanted desert.

"If you want a drink, there is milk and Coke over there in the fridge, just help yourselves." Sure enough, there was an open fridge, full of bottles of milk and Coca Cola.

The whole experience was marred by one problem. Bob did not think much of the idea of hamburger laced with cream! In the RAF you had a plate for each part of your meal, but they were now to find out how the Americans did things. No plates, just a large stainless steel tray with indentations in it for the different parts of your meal. Unfortunately, someone jogged Bob's elbow, hence the cream in the hamburger. This did not spoil the experience, however, and a group of extremely well fed and watered Erks finally retired to bed, determined to repeat the experience the following night.

After a similar breakfast experience they were back on the road and heading for the outskirts of London. The MT boys had done their homework and they arrived at another USAAF Base. This one looked less modern than last night's accommodation and appeared to have been a British Forces base fairly recently. The Guard Room directed them to their hut and apologised that it was not up to their usual standard. When they walked into the small concrete building, two things struck them straight away – there was the familiar pot-bellied stove in the centre of the room and the heat was on. When they investigated further they discovered the stove was oil fired, hence the heat, no stoking and cleaning for the Americans.

The eating experience turned out to be similar to the previous evening, but surprise-surprise, as they were visitors they had to pay one shilling each for their breakfast. This did not worry them too much, as they were planning to claim for the two nights on their Form 1771 anyway.

It was during this trip that Bob had his first experience of Police escorts. They were going to drive round the southern outskirts of London and it had been arranged for a Police escort to collect them from a lay-by just after their night stop.

When Bob had first joined the MU, the Queen Marys had been pulled by very ancient Crossley tractor units. These were draughty, slow and extremely noisy vehicles, conversation being impossible on the road. In addition they did around four miles to the gallon and frequent refuelling stops were necessary. They had recently been replaced by brand new Bedford units. These were quiet, fast, and even had heaters. The drivers enjoyed their two-speed axles that in effect gave them eight forward gears.

They met up with their escort, as arranged, this consisting of two traffic cars and two motorcyclists. The first question the Police drivers asked was, "How fast is your vehicle, driver?"

Bobs driver said that 45 to 50 mph was about the maximum, and that comment set the scene for the rest of the journey. The Police set off at a fair pace, turning off or blocking traffic lights and junctions. The lads in the trucks felt like Royalty. Skirting London at a steady 40mph was no mean task, especially considering the speed limit for all commercial vehicles was 30 mph and some were limited to 20mph. The journey passed without incident, apart from the tail plane of Bob's load removing the orange globe of a zebra crossing. They stopped, but their escort waved them on.

They arrived at their destination, RAF Cardbrook, this being a unit that trained aircraft loaders, hence the delivery of a current transport aircraft by 99MU. Now there were about a dozen of them by this time and they were directed to a billet in the main accommodation area.

On the first morning they knew they had to await the arrival of a mobile crane from their base before they could start work and so they decided there was no rush to get to breakfast. The Tannoy made the normal noises at 06.30, but the lads treated it with their normal deaf ear and turned over. About ten minutes later the door crashed open and two "Snowdrops" clattered in.

"Reveille lads, you have got ten minutes to get out of your pits." In true 99MU fashion they ignored this bluff, but bluff it was not and ten minutes later the SP's were back and they were all put on a charge.

Sgt Taffy Bottle was in charge of their gang and he made a phone call to base. This was obviously successful because when they eventually appeared in front of Cardbrook's CO he said, "We had to take action because this is a training camp, we will move you to a hut away from the main units, you will not be disturbed there. Case dismissed."

The job finished and they returned to base, having been away for around two months.

A few days after he arrived back, Bob bumped into Roy Thompson as he was coming out of the Flight Office, looking a bit sheepish.

"Problem?" asked Bob.

"Yes," said Roy. "I have just had a right dressing down by Chiefy Meakin."

When Bob asked what it was all about, Roy said it was a long story. It seems he had been down to an airfield near Cheltenham to dismantle a Spitfire and bring it back to base. They had loaded the aircraft onto a Queen Mary and prepared for the journey back through Cheltenham to Brister. Roy was "Second Man" on the load and had persuaded the driver to let him ride in the aircraft cockpit as they drove through Cheltenham. Roy then proceeded to give the Royal Wave to the people of Cheltenham as they passed slowly through the town. A Spitfire always attracted an audience wherever it went, but one with an Airman waving from the cockpit was an added attraction. Both the driver and Roy giggled about it all the way back and enjoyed sharing the story with their mates.

"Did he land it there Mummy?"

This, it turned out, had happened about a week ago and this morning Roy had been called into the Flight Office. As he walked in there was a copy of the *Cheltenham Gazette* on Flt Sgt Meakins desk and there, in pride of place, was a photograph of Roy, waving happily to the shoppers of Cheltenham. It seems that Flt Sgt Meakins' brother-in-law lived in Cheltenham and had sent Chiefy a copy of the paper.

You just can't help bad luck! Although Roy had received a good dressing down, he was sure a smile was lurking on Chiefy's face.

Roy Thomson seemed to be one of those people that had everything happen to them. A few months earlier he had been part of a small gang that had collected a single engined training aircraft from a private airfield where it had made an emergency landing. The rest of the gang went straight onto another job and Roy and a driver delivered the aircraft back to its home base. It seems the fog came down during the afternoon and they became ever so slightly lost. They stopped at a local Police station and were directed to a nearby Army camp for the night.

They crept through the fog and eventually arrived at the Guard Room. The duty officer arranged accommodation for them and told a young Sapper to direct them to the car park. This young gentleman was evidently from Glasgow, although he may as well have been from Timbuktu, because neither Roy nor the driver could understand a word he said. He rattled off the directions and then promptly disappeared into the fog. They crept around the road in the direction the Sapper had pointed and found a wide tarmac area suitable for parking the Queen Mary. They decided to give the cookhouse a miss and went straight to the Naafi and had egg and chips and a mug of tea. They were going to make an early start the next day and so turned in quite early.

At some unearthly hour, just as it was getting light, they were woken up by an almighty crash as the door flew open and a khaki-clad figure with no eyes and suffering from head lice strode in. Well he may have had eyes but they were hidden behind the peak of his cap and he obviously shaved his head to get rid of lice.

"Who the *!#x!* #%$ has parked their %$£&~! lorry in the middle of my @#$££&* parade ground? Shift it NOW!"

The sight of an MT driver in his pyjamas running across the parade ground to move his vehicle was a sight to behold, evidently.

So, having escaped the wrath of the gentleman, who they discovered was the RSM, they got back on the road. The driver said, "I have looked at the map and we can take a short cut back to the A41 to avoid the town. Roy checked his load and off they went, along what was a fairly wide country lane. They rounded a bend and there in front of them was – a low bridge!

"Don't worry," said the driver. "We will probably get through if we use the centre of the road. You will have to ride on the trailer while I creep forward and you watch me through."

They eased up to the bridge but the top of the aircraft tail was about two inches too high, so they stopped and had a re-think. There was no way they could turn around in the narrow road so Roy had a bright idea.

"Why not let the trailer tyres down just enough to get through?"

"Ok," said the driver, "But how do we pump them up again afterwards?"

They looked at the trailer, the bridge and the aircraft and the driver said, "I have a better idea; let's lower the aircraft."

Now this was an aircraft with a large radial engine still installed and the aircraft was supported on three trestles, one under the engine, one under the tail and one in the middle.

"If we lower the rear trestle a few inches and tighten down the strop that goes over the rear fuselage, it would pivot the tail down," said the driver.

They agreed that this was the thing to do, so they lowered the rear trestle and tightened up the turnbuckle on the strop.

Bingo! It worked, and they edged their way through the arch and pulled into a lay-by to put everything back together.

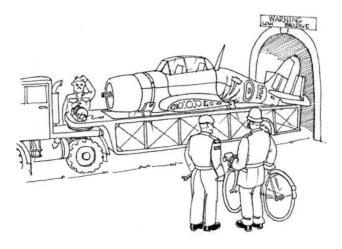

"Should it be that shape lad?"

By this time, although it was a country road, quite a bit of traffic had built up and the local Bobby had turned up on his push bike to supervise things. Having got things organised he was leaning on his bike, watching them sort their load out when he said, "That was a clever bit of work there lads, but should there really be wrinkles in the skin of the rear fuselage?"

Then real horror struck Roy. The weight of the engine, together with pulling down on the tail, had distorted the fuselage. The policeman rode off and left them debating their fate. They decide to reverse the process and raise the tail. This seemed to solve the problem, so they secured the load and made their way to their destination, but all the time Roy was panicking that he really should report the problem. What would happen if the plane crashed and he was responsible?

They arrived at the Flying Training School without further incident and while they were unloading the aircraft, the Engineering Officer and the CO turned up to inspect the aircraft for damage following its emergency landing. Roy was about to approach them and come clean when the Engineering Officer said to his colleague, "It must have been quite a heavy landing sir, the rear fuselage has been distorted, it will have to go down as a write-off."

Roy heaved a sigh of relief and went to find the driver and share the good news.

This incident was one of many in the years that Bob spent at RAF Brister, but he was now nearing the end of his service and he had to decide his future. If he wanted promotion he had to sign on for at least another four years, or he could leave and take his chance in the outside world. The twins were probably married now and, let's face it, there were plenty of Waafs to choose from.

While he was lying on his bed, trying to work out his options, Brummy Wheeler walked in. Bob explained that he was trying to decide what to do and asked Brummy how much longer he had to the end of his service

"Only fifty eight days and a late breakfast mate," was the reply.

~ END ~

*"No they are not revising, they are
working out how many days to demob."*

If you have enjoyed this book, why not take a look at some of the other books of RAF and military humour available from Woodfield?

Upside Down, Nothing On the Clock ~ a fun-filled collection of true stories and jokes contributed by all ranks of the RAF.   £6.00

Upside Down Again ~ another enjoyable collection of RAF and aviation humour.   £6.00

Was It Like This For You? ~ RAF veterans recall the absurdities of service life in words and cartoons.   £6.00

Those Bloomin' Snowdrops! ~ Former RAF Police personnel reveal the bizarre and hilarious situations they encountered in the line of duty in an enjoyable collection of stories and cartoons.   £9.95

I Have Control? ~ True stories featuring the funny side life in the RAF, guaranteed to amuse any veteran of the armed forces.   £9.95

Who Is In Charge Here? ~ More amusing real-life tales highlighting the funny side of life in the military.   £9.95

Carry On Corporal ~ Yet more true tales poking fun at the many absurd aspects of life in the armed forces.   £9.95

Naafi, Knickers and Nijmegen ~ A humorous and nostalgic recollection of life in the postwar WRAF   £9.95

Why Did We Join? ~ A light-hearted look at what life was like for the young women who served in the wartime WAAF   £9.95

Woodfield have published many more books featuring the RAF and its history ~ plus many other subjects

Visit our website for full details, special offers and more...

www.woodfieldpublishing.co.uk